WHI
NATIVE

**New Zealand Native Trees – A Simple Guide
to their Identification, Ecology and Uses**

ANDREW CROWE

PENGUIN BOOKS

Introduction to Ecology Edition

Visitors to this country rarely leave without being impressed by the ancient feel of the native forest. Massive mature trees hold aloft perching plants to rival those of tropical rainforest, with a flora that is almost entirely evergreen; with tree ferns and a native palm. For a temperate country, it all seems strangely tropical – a reminder that this landmass once lay closer to the equator. Millions of years of geological isolation in the absence of land mammals has also provided unique conditions for the vegetation to develop many unusual species. Eighty percent of the trees, ferns and flowering plants here are found nowhere else.

Since the first editions of these books were written, there has been a significant growth in tourism, bringing with it a new pride and interest in New Zealand's native flora. Many native plants are now available in garden centres. Revegetation projects and native theme gardens are no longer unusual. With this has come a renewed interest in how the whole system interconnects – how the pieces of the jigsaw of nature fit together. These new editions of *Which Native Tree?*, *Which Native Fern?* and *Which Native Forest Plant?* (used in conjunction with the bird and insect identification books in this series) are designed to respond to this need.

BIRDS, LIZARDS AND BATS Many of New Zealand's native birds depend on specific native trees for nectar or fruit or as a source of nesting material. Likewise, lizards, bats and insects feed on the nectar. In return, most of these creatures provide some kind of service to the tree: pollination in the case of nectar feeders or, in the case of those feeding on the fruit, transport of seeds. Over millions of years, this relationship has come to a kind of balance in which all parties continue to survive. However, this ancient forest and its wildlife have a new challenge: they are not so well adapted to the newcomers – people, possums, pigs, deer, goats, rats, mice, stoats and wasps.

INSECTS AND MITES Less well-known, however, is the fact that many New Zealand native trees also have at least one kind of native insect that, at some stage in its life cycle, depends on that tree for food. Many of these unique little creatures are active only at night so are seldom seen, but their presence is often evident from chew marks on the leaves, for example. Torn leaves are likely to be possum damage, but nibble marks and holes are often the result of feeding insects (little beetles, or caterpillars of moths, for example); pale squiggly lines within the leaves are a tell-tale sign of tunnelling maggots of specialist 'leafminer flies' or the tiny caterpillars of specialist 'leafminer moths'. Other tiny critters will leave distinctive lumps ('galls') on the plant.

FLOWER COLOURS There are few large or colourful flowers in the New Zealand forest; bright reds, blues and purples are almost entirely absent. This is due to the colour perception of local pollinators, most of which are insects. New Zealand has few butterflies, for example, more than twice the number of fly species of comparable countries, a third the number of wasps and bees, and no native long-tongued bees.

Blue and **purple** flowers generally attract butterflies and introduced bees.

Red flowers in the New Zealand native flora are either large and adapted for bird pollination, or small and adapted for visits by flies and native bees.

Yellow flowers are generally good at drawing flies, native bees and beetles.

White is the colour of most New Zealand native flowers; these flowers are often tiny, conspicuous only by being crowded together. By day, this suits the flies. At night, white catches the moonlight, attracting the attention of moths – especially if the flower is scented.

Green flowers are also common in New Zealand. Many of these are small and scented, making them attractive to flies in particular.

Using this Book

The simplest way to identify New Zealand native trees is by their leaves; this is because almost all retain their leaves year round.

A few simple points about using these leaf keys

Basically, there are three ways in which leaves (or leaflets) are arranged on a branch or stalk: hand-shaped, alternating or opposite.

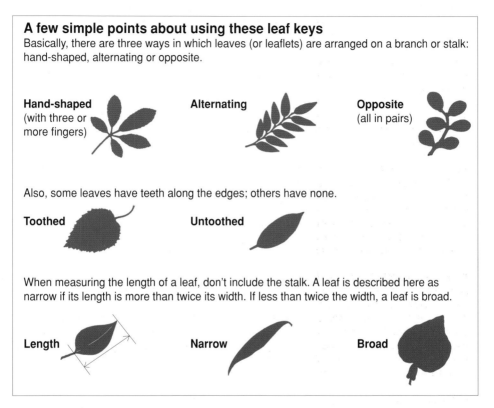

Hand-shaped (with three or more fingers)

Alternating

Opposite (all in pairs)

Also, some leaves have teeth along the edges; others have none.

Toothed

Untoothed

When measuring the length of a leaf, don't include the stalk. A leaf is described here as narrow if its length is more than twice its width. If less than twice the width, a leaf is broad.

Length

Narrow

Broad

To use the leaf keys

1 Find a typical leaf of a common adult, native tree. Don't pull it off because later you'll need to look at how it grows on the tree. Now turn to page 5 and decide which type of leaf it is. Starting at the bottom of the chart, turn to the page indicated.
2 Follow the arrow at the bottom of this new page to take you up the appropriate branch until you arrive at an illustration of your leaf. Now turn to the page indicated for a close-up photograph of that leaf.
3 To double-check your initial identification, use the checklist next to the photograph.

If you have any trouble (like not being able to reach the leaves, or being unable to match your leaf to the key), turn to Troubleshooting on page 62.

* To be precise, trees have either 'simple' leaves or 'compound' ones made up of individual 'leaflets'. However, the layperson (and this book) generally refers to both leaves and leaflets simply as 'leaves'. Later, you may want to know the difference between a simple leaf and a group of leaflets that makes up a compound leaf: leaf buds are the clue. If you find a bud at its base, then it is a leaf and not a leaflet. (Examples of compound leaves in this book are kohekohe, tītoki, kōwhai, patete, whauwhaupaku and pūriri.)

Using the tree pages

For simplicity, trees that look similar appear on facing pages. Use the identification checklists on these pages to distinguish between them. The following graphics show the usual distribution and common size for each tree.

A guide to the approximate range within which the wild tree may be found.

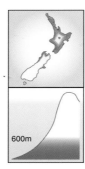

A guide to the altitudes where the tree naturally grows (in metres).

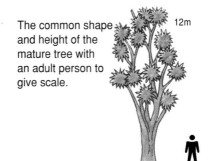

The common shape and height of the mature tree with an adult person to give scale.

Another approach: the flowers and berries key

If the tree has large, conspicuous flowers or fruits, you can also take a more direct approach: turn to page 61. What colour is the flower or fruit? Follow that colour up the tree diagram until you arrive at the appropriate flower or fruit. Turn to the page indicated and double-check using the checklist on that page.

Māori names

This book encourages the reader to be on 'first name' terms with the trees. Note, however, that many of these names are regional. It is necessary in a book like this to keep to the Māori names most widely used, but tribal variations are just as valid. Note that names like kahikatea, tōtara, mānuka and tītoki are often mispronounced, so a little help is given. The correct pronunciation of Māori vowels is as follows: 'a' as in 'far', 'e' as in 'bet', 'i' as in 'me', 'o' as in 'or', 'u' as in 'flu'. To help with getting the length of the vowels correct, macrons have been included; these indicate a lengthened vowel,
e.g. ā = aa, ē = ee, ī = ii, ō = oo, ū = uu. Thus 'Māori' is pronounced 'Maaori'.

Cultural uses

Knowing about the uses of trees can be great for fostering an appreciation of them, but it can also lead to thoughtless damage. For example, taking bark from a living tree for, say, wool dyeing or medicine can easily kill that tree. The maxim displayed in many publicly owned forests could be taken as a general rule:

Take only photographs;
leave only footprints.

Of course, this should apply equally to governments and companies wishing to mill and mine our dwindling wilderness and to those who advocate carving roads through what remains of them. Corporate bodies need to be encouraged from without and within to set a good example.

Ecology

The study of ecology involves patient observation. There is a lot still to be learnt in this field and the observant reader (young or old) has a good chance of making new discoveries – especially with the aid of a camera and good record-keeping. (See pages 2 and 63 for more on forest ecology.)

Insects etc. in the margins

Creatures, berries and flowers etc., whose names appear in red type indicate those whose illustration can be found on that page. Wherever possible, these are shown life-size. However, photos of birds, lizards, possums and mice are, of course, reduced.

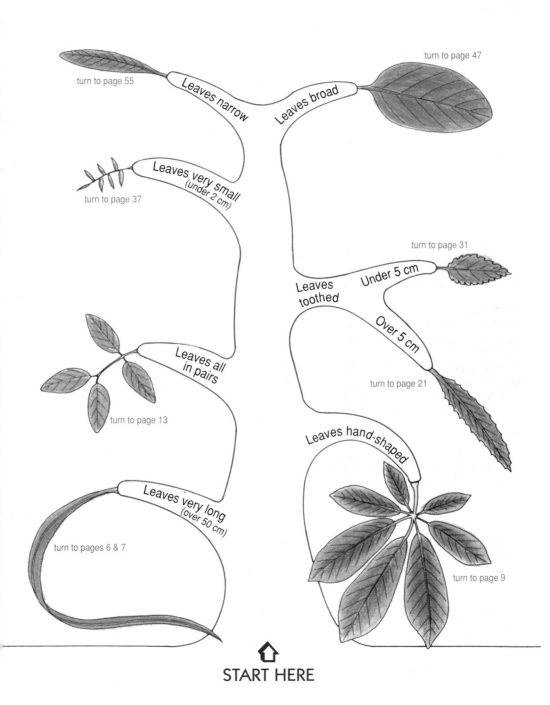

turn to page 55

Leaves narrow

Leaves broad

turn to page 47

Leaves very small
(under 2 cm)

turn to page 37

turn to page 31

Leaves
toothed

Under 5 cm

Over 5 cm

turn to page 21

Leaves all
in pairs

turn to page 13

Leaves hand-shaped

Leaves very long
(over 50 cm)

turn to pages 6 & 7

turn to page 9

⬆
START HERE

Tī Kōuka
Cabbage Tree

Cordyline australis [Family: Agavaceae]

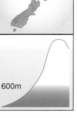

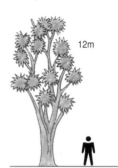

12m

600m

Leaves:	Narrow, *grass-like*, 50 cm–1 m long, growing in tufts
Flowers:	White, sweetly scented (late spring)
Fruit:	Small, bluish-white (late summer)
Trunk:	*Spongy to squeeze*, like cork
Other:	Common in swamps and flood plains. Similar species are found in forest

Also known as **ti kāuka**. Tī is the tropical Polynesian term for the related Pacific Island cabbage tree (*Cordyline fruticosa*); kōuka ('withstands wind'); kāuka ('withstands fire') – both true. The cooked tap roots, the core of the trunk and tender shoots were important Māori foods. The roots and stems are rich in sugar (*fructose*), but tests carried out in the mid-1980s indicated that as a food sugar crop the tree had little chance of being commercially viable. The leaves provided Māori with a source of strong fibre for weaving baskets, making bird snares, rope and string, rain capes, sandals and thatching. Leaf scrapings were applied to cuts and sores, and leaves brewed into a tea used as a cure for dysentery and diarrhoea. In the 1860s, paper made from the leaves received high praise at one of England's largest paper-mills, but excessive cartage costs thwarted a commercial venture. Fallen branches, complete with leaf heads, are still used by rural children today as makeshift sledges on grassy farmland slopes.

Nature Notes: In spring, geckos forage in the flowers, as do native flies and honey bees. The small fruit is popular with korimako (bellbirds) and kererū (New Zealand pigeons), while kahu (Australasian harriers) collect leaves to line their nests. In spring and summer, the 'cabbage tree moth' (top) rests well-camouflaged on the underside of dead leaves; its flat green caterpillars (top right) hide in the soft leaf bases by day, coming out at night to chew notches and holes in the leaves. The caterpillar of another specialist moth, the 'cabbage tree bell moth' (right), curls the tips of the youngest leaves to form a sheltering tube. Within the leaves live grubs of the 'Cordyline weevil'. Since the late 1980s, many trees have been dying from a disease called 'sudden decline', caused by a phytoplasma (*Phytoplasma australiense*) carried by planthopper insects feeding on the sap. Young trees are freely eaten by goats and deer.

Growing It: Planted in small groups for subtropical effect, or grown as a tub plant, cabbage trees are best placed away from lawns and buildings to prevent falling leaves becoming a nuisance. Grows easily and quickly from seed but beware of pūkeko pulling out young plants to eat their roots. Can also be grown from cuttings. Tolerant of wind, fire and possums. Several cultivated forms are available.

Nīkau

Rhopalostylis sapida [Family: Arecaceae]

10m

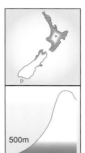

500m

Leaves:	*Palm fronds*
Flowers:	Small and pink, hanging in long spreading fingers (late spring to early autumn)
Fruit:	Small, red, in finger-like bunches (mostly late summer/ early autumn)
Trunk:	With circular leaf scars, often with a fringe of prop roots at the base

'Nīkau' is the east Polynesian term for 'coconut frond', for, although the New Zealand equivalent of the coconut proved to be barren, its fronds still proved suitable as a roofing material and leaf strips could be woven into kete (baskets). The heart of the palm (undeveloped leaves) was an occasional Māori food, eaten raw or cooked and sometimes taken medicinally to ease childbirth; however, its removal kills the tree. The pink immature flowers, while still enclosed in their green sheaths, are likewise edible but with less cost to the tree. In a survival emergency, it is also possible to slit a hole in the base of the bulbous swelling at the top of the trunk to drink collected rainwater as it drains out. The ripe, red fruit consists mostly of hard seed, so hard that when other forms of ammunition were scarce, these were used by settlers for bird shooting. The rounded base of fallen fronds makes a very attractive bowl-like container, especially when polished or stained with wax. Rural children use them too on grassy slopes as sledges. At 44°S on the Chatham Islands, nīkau can claim to be the world's southernmost palm.

Nature Notes: Stitchbirds, native flies and honey bees visit the flowers. Possums eat flowerbuds and berries but seldom the fronds. Kākā, kākāriki (parakeets), kiore (Pacific rats) and ship rats eat the fruit, while kiwi, kererū, kōkako, blackbirds and song thrushes spread the seeds by swallowing them whole. Kiwi use seeds as gizzard stones. Kererū often nest in the tops; other birds remove leaf fibre as nesting material. Stored rainwater trickling from the top keeps the trunk moist for mosses and lance ferns to thrive. Caterpillars of the 'nīkau moth' drill the fruit and hard seeds. Grubs of one 'nīkau weevil' live in the green bases of leaves. Fallen fronds support four other 'nīkau weevils', the 'nīkau anthribid' fungus weevil (right), Peripatus ('walking worm'), small native landsnails and almost 200 species of fungus. The bleeding gum attracts 'large pill beetles' (below right). Pigs uproot trees to reach the succulent heart.

Growing It: A very attractive and distinctively tropical landscaping tree, especially when planted as a grove, but sensitive to wind; withstands only light frosts. Best in rich, deep soil. Grown from seed – cover first with boiling water to soften the coating. Slow to germinate and very slow to produce a trunk.

LEAVES OVER 50 cm

Pūriri

Vitex lucens [Family: Verbenaceae]

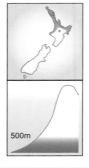

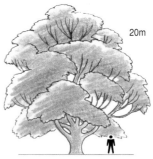

20m

500m

Leaves:	Hand-shaped, with 3–5 'fingers', *no teeth*, glossy, rippled between veins like waves in the sea, leaf stalks square-angled
Flowers:	Pinkish-red, 2.5 cm long (all year, but particularly in winter)
Fruit:	Round, red, 2 cm across (all year)
Trunk:	Heavily gnarled

Northland Māori considered pūriri sacred and buried the bones of their dead in and around old trees. An alternative name, **kauere** ('a rip in the sea'), describes the rippled texture of the leaf and trunk. An infusion of leaves was used for bathing muscular aches and sprains, and as a remedy for ulcers and sore throats. A compound found in the leaves (*p-hydroxybenzoic* acid) has since been used to manufacture a patented germicide. The bark provided Māori with *vitexin*, a source of yellow dye for colouring flax weaving, though it should be emphasised that stripping bark can easily destroy a living tree. An old name used by early European settlers, **New Zealand oak**, refers to the reputation of its wood being New Zealand's strongest and most durable (used for piles, fence posts, railway sleepers, bridges, etc.). Indeed, it proved so difficult to split that timber workers often resorted to using dynamite. Its swirling grain makes it a hard wood to work too, although fallen trees are still valued for woodturning.

Nature Notes: Primarily pollinated by birds attracted to the nectar: tūī, bellbirds, stitchbirds, kōkako, kākā and silvereyes. Of these, bellbirds are the most effective pollinators. Kākāriki eat both flowerbuds and flowers, while rats eat the flowers and fruit. Honey bees concentrate more on the pollen. Kererū (New Zealand pigeons) are an important disperser of the seeds, though the ripe fruit is also popular with tūī, kākā and kōkako. Perching plants are common on the branches. Larger cavities in trunks are used as nests by kākā, kākāriki and stitch-birds. Māori proverb tells of the constant battle (riri) this tree has with caterpillars of the 'pūriri moth' (pepe tuna) which make finger-sized holes in the lower half of the trunk (pū) – hence 'pūriri'. Inhabited holes are capped by webbing; those whose capping is removed indicate the caterpillar has gone – tunnelweb spiders or tree wētā will take over. Tiny lumps ('galls') on leaves are caused by two species of 'pūriri leaf mite'. Since the 1980s many old trees have been dying, not of possums but apparently as a result of the same phytoplasma that attacks cabbage trees.

Growing It: A useful shade or specimen tree. Grows easily from seed – cover first with boiling water and soak overnight to soften the coating. Can also be grown from side cuttings taken low down on the tree; include a chip of bark for best results. Best in rich deep soil with not too much shade.

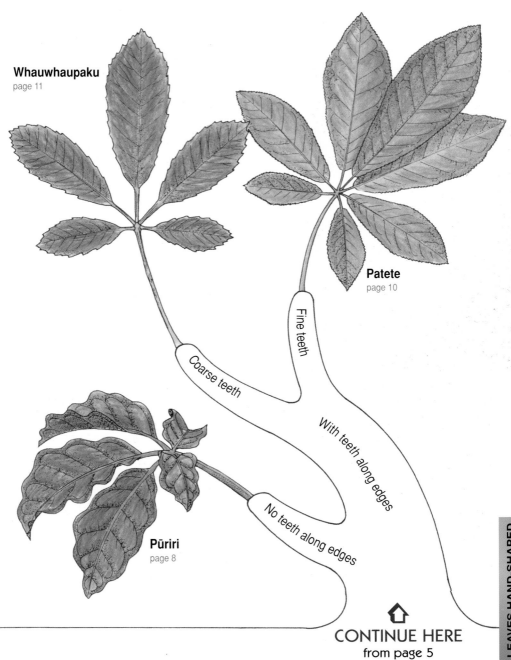

Whauwhaupaku
page 11

Patete
page 10

Fine teeth

Coarse teeth

With teeth along edges

Pūriri
page 8

No teeth along edges

⌂
CONTINUE HERE
from page 5

Patete
Seven Finger

Schefflera digitata [Family: Araliaceae]

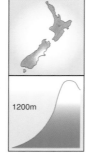

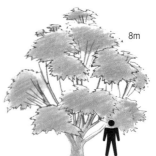

8m

1200m

Leaves:	Hand-shaped, with 7–9 'fingers', *fine* teeth, *thin*, *limp* (unlike whauwhaupaku, opposite)
Flowers:	Small, greenish, *hang in long fingers* (unlike whauwhaupaku) (late summer)
Fruit:	Very small, purple-black, in long fingers (on female trees only) in autumn
Other:	Found mainly along the edges of forest

Also known as **patē**. 'Patete' means 'itch', a symbolic allusion no doubt to the fingernails of the fire-goddess, Mahuika, for the tree's principal Māori use was for fire-making. Slabs of dry, soft wood (the itch) would be vigorously scratched with a pointed stick of a much harder wood (e.g. kaikōmako), wearing a groove in the patete slab until the accumulating dust caught alight. Other Māori uses include making popguns (pakoro) from the stems, a rod of mānuka being used as ammunition, and using the sap to heal ringworm and sores caused by tuberculosis of the lymph glands. The leaves contain *falcarindiol* which has the specific effect of inhibiting germination of the spores of common skin fungi, such as those that cause ringworm. The leaves of patete were also used (along with large-leaved coprosma and hen and chickens fern) for wrapping newborn babies until they perspired. European settlers used the berries for dyeing wool.

Nature Notes: With the aid of what is known as the 'flag effect', bunches of small pale flowers attract small flies and occasionally birds, including bellbirds and stitchbirds. The small fruit is eaten by tūī, bellbirds, kererū (New Zealand pigeons), kōkako, stitchbirds, saddlebacks, silvereyes and ship rats. Kōkako will also tear off leaves, which they take to a perch to pick off 'sixpenny scale insects'. In the warmer months, 'patē owlet' moth caterpillars gather by day under the leaves (of patete and houhere), emerging at night to feed on these. Specialist insects include the 'Araliad mirid' insect (which sucks the sap); grubs of the 'Araliad weevil' (which tunnel below the bark of dying trees), and grubs of the 'patē weevil' (in living bark). The 'New Zealand vegetable bug' (a shiny native version of the vegetable pest) is sometimes found sucking the sap. Roots are a common host to the parasitic, flowering *Dactylanthus* wood rose (pua reinga). Young trees and foliage are freely eaten by goats, cattle and deer.

Growing It: Patete is recommended for planting to attract birds, and is a favourite for its tropical appearance. Grows best in reasonable soil with some shade and is propagated either by seed or from cuttings. Leaves of the North Island seedlings are often attractively lobed like long oak leaves.

Whauwhaupaku
Five Finger

Pseudopanax arboreus [Family: Araliaceae]

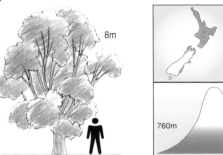

8m

760m

Leaves:	Hand-shaped, with 5–7 'fingers', *large* teeth, *thick and leathery* (unlike patete, opposite)
Flowers:	Tiny, sweet scented, in ball-like clusters (winter)
Fruit:	Tiny, black, in ball-like clusters (on female trees only) in spring
Other:	The more southern **orihou** (**mountain five finger**) usually has no stalks on its 'fingers'

A clear, tasteless, jelly-like gum often oozes from the growing bud and this apparently is what inspired the tree's former Taranaki name '**snotty gob**' – a feature also referred to in Māori names **parapara** or **tauparapara** ('parapara' meaning 'spittle'). 'Whauwhau' in the name 'whauwhaupaku' (also **houhou**, and 'hou' in the Bay of Plenty name **puahou**) may refer to the criss-crossing lace-like fibres of the inner bark that closely resemble those of houhere (lacebark). The bark was used to make small water-carrying containers. For Tūhoe Māori, the tree's fruiting marked the fourth month of the calendar (September). Even the ripe berries are inedible (tasting extremely bitter), but these do make reasonably good wool dyes: purple, khaki, green, grey or mauve, depending on the mordant used. More recently, chemists have discovered antiviral properties in the leaves, effective against influenza type A.

Nature Notes: Tūī, bellbirds, stitchbirds, kākā, native flies and honey bees all collect the nectar. Tūī, bellbirds, kererū (New Zealand pigeons), kākā, kākāriki, tīeke (saddlebacks), hihi (stitchbirds), kōkako, silvereyes and weka eat the fruit. Possums chew flowers and leaves, but seem to be particularly fond of biting out the base of the leaf stalks. Look out for the remains of the leaf that they invariably let drop to the forest floor. Plants are also freely eaten by goats, cattle and deer. Seedling trees are commonly found perching in tree ferns, from where they will eventually send their roots down to the

ground. The hairy, green caterpillars of the 'five finger plume moth' often chew leaves, as do the looper caterpillars of the 'North Island lichen moth' ('zebra moth' top left) and those of the 'five finger looper' moth. Several tiny caterpillars specialise in mining the leaves or stems. Lumps on leaves are left by a psyllid insect, an 'Araliad mirid' insect sucks the sap, and the grubs of at least nine kinds of 'five finger weevil' tunnel the bark.

Growing It: An attractive specimen tree or shrub that will also grow well in a tub or pot. Very hardy, withstanding wind. It looks best when fed well to produce larger leaves. Grows easily from fresh, ripe seed or semi-hardwood cuttings (taken from partially matured wood just after a new flush of growth).

LEAVES HAND-SHAPED

11

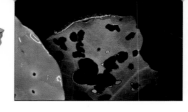

Kawakawa
Macropiper excelsum [Family: Piperaceae]

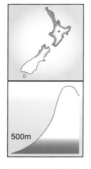

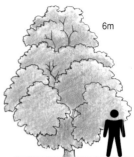

6m

500m

Leaves:	Opposite, *heart-shaped* (unlike most native trees), *spicy smell* when crushed, usually full of holes
Fruit:	Yellow-orange, usually 2–5 cm long (on female trees only), mostly in summer
Other:	Purplish-brown branches, *jointed like crooked bamboo*

Kawakawa is related to the kava of Fiji, to which its Māori name is ultimately linked. Likewise, an alternative European name, '**pepper tree**', refers to the fact that this plant is related also to the true pepper tree of Indonesia. Māori gardeners laid wet, green kawakawa leaves and branches between kūmara beds and set fire to them, using the acrid smoke to poison pest insects. Research confirms that the leaves and branches do contain insecticidal compounds including one that can kill many insects by interfering with their metamorphoses. One insect with a peculiar immunity to this is the 'kawakawa looper' caterpillar, whose holes are commonly seen in the leaves. In this case, the plant has shown its ability to take its defence a step further by responding to artificial leaf damage by increasing its toxicity. Māori ate the ripe, orange fruit, which tastes sweet and was sometimes used to flavour a kind of jelly made from seaweed. (If you dislike the spicy taste of the tiny, black seeds, you may wish to spit these out.) These days, leaves are often brewed to make a herbal tea. In the long list of medicinal uses of the plant is at least one – chewing the leaves to alleviate toothache – that is known to have a sound chemical basis. The plant's essential oil contains *myristicin*, a substance similar to the pain-numbing constituent of cloves. The branches and leaves have been used by spinners to produce green dyes.

Nature Notes: At night, geckos and skinks will fight for the fruit, which is popular by day with kererū (New Zealand pigeon), tūī, kākā, saddlebacks, kōkako, blackbirds, weka, kiore (Pacific rat) and ship rats. In spring and summer, caterpillars of the 'kawakawa looper' moth can often be seen on the underside of leaves, commonly eating holes in them. Two kinds of 'kawakawa gall mite' make small lumps on the leaves. Kawakawa is freely eaten by goats, deer and kiore, but possums are put off by the high concentration of compounds known as *terpenes*.

Growing It: Tolerates shade or sun and the occasional pruning, has an attractive compact shape and can be grown in a tub or pot or even as a hedge. Grows quickly from seed or cuttings. Does best with well-drained soil and shelter from frost.

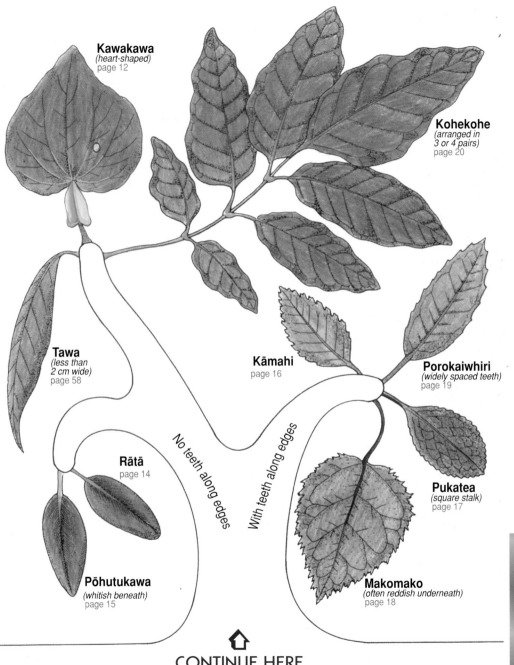

Kawakawa
(heart-shaped)
page 12

Kohekohe
(arranged in 3 or 4 pairs)
page 20

Tawa
(less than 2 cm wide)
page 58

Kāmahi
page 16

Porokaiwhiri
(widely spaced teeth)
page 19

No teeth along edges

With teeth along edges

Rātā
page 14

Pukatea
(square stalk)
page 17

Pōhutukawa
(whitish beneath)
page 15

Makomako
(often reddish underneath)
page 18

⬆
CONTINUE HERE
from page 5

Rātā
Northern
Metrosideros robusta [Family: Myrtaceae]
Southern
Metrosideros umbellata [Family: Myrtaceae]

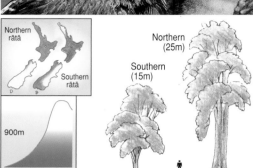

Northern rātā / Southern rātā

900m

Northern (25m)
Southern (15m)

Leaves:	Opposite, *green underneath* (unlike pōhutukawa), leaf tips on **northern rātā** indented and rounder than **southern rātā**
Flowers:	Red, in spiky balls (summer)
Other:	**Northern rātā** often grows high in the forks of other trees, sending roots down to engulf its dead or dying host. **Southern rātā** is a medium-sized tree, starting as a seed in the ground

A rākau rangatira (chiefly tree), whose name was brought here by the ancestors of New Zealand Māori from tropical Polynesia, where rātā is a traditional term for *Metrosideros* trees. Māori used the timber for weapons, paddles, mauls and traditional flutes. Its hardness, strength and durability later made it suitable for everything from machine bearings, shipbuilding and bridge construction to cartwheels, carving-chisel handles and woodturning. It was also very highly recommended as firewood. An infusion of inner bark was used as a remedy for diarrhoea; the bark has indeed since been shown to contain *ellagic* acid – an astringent against diarrhoea and dysentery. The outer bark has medicinal uses too, and was recommended to tanners for its high tannin content. Homespinners have used this for dyeing wool. The nectar was used by Māori both as food and as a remedy for sore throats. It is interesting then to see that the flowers have since been shown to contain antiseptics such as *gallic* acid.

Nature Notes: At night, short-tailed bats and lizards visit the flowers for nectar; by day, come tūī, bellbirds, stitchbirds, silvereyes, kākā, kea, even kākāpō, and bees (both native and introduced). In late winter, kākā peck trapdoors in the bark of southern rātā to tap the sap. Kākāriki eat flowerbuds and flowers, while leaves are relished by native stick insects and possums; indeed, 1950–1990, possums led to whole forests dying, prompting conservationists to climb trunks of some older trees to place metal bands around them; this has proven effective in saving many. Young trees are also freely eaten by goats and deer. The tiny grub of a 'rātā leafminer weevil' tunnels its way through the inside of the leaf; the grubs of another four kinds of 'rātā weevils' feed in the bark and dead wood. Native caterpillars found on the leaves include those of the 'common forest looper' moth. Conspicuous among the many plants found perching in the branches are flax-like native astelias, kahakaha and kiekie.

Growing It: Both types of rātā can be grown as garden plants, but with the disadvantage of taking many years to produce flowers. Southern rātā is smaller and better suited to colder climates.

Listed uses refer primarily to northern rātā, but southern rātā can, in many cases, be used in the same way.

Pōhutukawa

Metrosideros excelsa [Family: Myrtaceae]

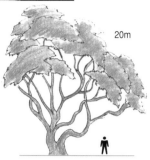

20m

mainly coastal

Leaves:	Opposite (unlike karo), *velvety white underneath* (unlike rātā), 5–8 cm long
Flowers:	Red, in large spiky balls (early summer – Christmas time)
Trunk:	Gnarled and spreading
Other:	Often noticed on coastal cliffs; *branchlets white*; curtains of aerial roots are often seen hanging from the branches

Māori collected nectar for food and as a treatment for sore throats. To get a taste try poking your tongue into the flower as the birds do. An infusion of inner bark was used to cure dysentery and diarrhoea; indeed, pōhutukawa contains *ellagic* acid, an astringent used for both ailments. The deep red timber is extremely strong and durable, used from the earliest time of European settlement for making stems and knees in boatbuilding. A dense, hard-wearing wood, it was used in bearings and machine beds, framing and sills of dock gates and the like. It burns well. Tourist guides sometimes refer to it as the **New Zealand Christmas tree**. The Māori name comes from the southern Cook Islands where it refers a coastal tree with almost identical leaves.

Nature Notes: By moonlight, short-tailed bats and Pacific geckos feed in the flowers, but with sunrise provide nectar for kākā, tūī, bellbirds, stitchbirds, sparrows and bees (introduced and native); kākāriki eat whole flowers and seed capsules. Since the 1980s, the tree's survival in the wild has been threatened by possums browsing new growth. The leaves are also a favourite food of the 'common stick insect'. On both sides of the leaf, little lumps (galls) are left by the 'rātā gall mite', but more prominent lumps seen on leaves of young trees (above) are made by the 'pōhutukawa psyllid' insect. Among many other insects on the tree are the caterpillars of the 'pōhutukawa seed moth' (which feed inside seed capsules), a 'rātā leafminer weevil' (whose grub tunnels inside of the leaf itself), and three 'pōhutukawa scale' insects. Large holes in the upper trunk of mature trees provide nesting sites for kākā, kākāriki and stitchbird; branches of coastal trees are a favourite roosting site for shag colonies.

Growing It: Grows naturally only in northern regions, but widely planted (often as a coastal tree) as far south as Dunedin. A great specimen tree, it prunes well so is also used for hedging. Semi-hardwood cuttings have the advantage of bypassing the tender juvenile stage and flowering much sooner. Also easily grown from the fresh seed which is fine and dust-like. In February or March, hold a bag over a cluster of seed capsules and shake to collect these. Sow thinly.

Kāmahi

Weinmannia racemosa [Family: Cunoniaceae]

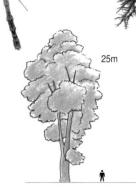

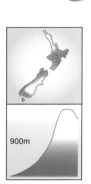

25m

900m

Leaves:	*Opposite* (unlike beech), 3–10 cm long (smaller and less leathery on juveniles) with large teeth
Flowers:	Almost white, fluffy, in finger-like clusters (late spring/ early summer)
Other:	North of Auckland a slightly smaller-leaved form is found, called **tōwai**

Kāmahi is known as a pyrophytic tree, meaning that it is often dominant after a fire, 'kā' meaning 'burn' and 'mahi' 'abundance'. Māori used the bark to make a black dye for colouring flax and cabbage tree leaves. The air-dried bark of young trees contains over 8% tannin (older trees: double this), providing 19th century leather tanners with one of the country's richest native sources of tannin and a primary raw material that – for a few years during the 19th century – was even exported. In Māori medicine, the inner bark was steeped in hot water and the liquid drunk as a laxative; the bark itself, with its astringent tannins and *catechin*, was infused as a tonic. Chemical analysis has identified in the leaves antiviral properties against influenza type A. As a timber, kāmahi was put to many below-ground uses (piles, fence posts, sleepers, etc.), and its figured wood is sometimes used by woodturners. However, as cabinetmakers discovered, it tends to warp badly, and large diameter logs required for milling boards were frequently hollow. Florists occasionally use the foliage in formal flower arrangements.

Nature Notes: Tūī, bellbirds, stitchbirds and honey bees visit the flowers for nectar. Flowers, seeds and leaves are all eaten by kererū. The leaves, being high in *phenols*, are relished by possums, leading since the 1950s to the collapse of entire forests. It is also freely eaten by goats and deer. Two species of stick insects are commonly found here and the following specialist invertebrates: a couple of 'kāmahi scale' insects (one on the leaves and one on stems), the tiny maggots of the 'kāmahi gall midge' (damages young leaves) and two kinds of 'kāmahi weevil' grub (tunnelling within dead leaves). Looper caterpillars on green leaves are likely to be those of the 'kāmahi green spindle' moth. Four times as many insects climb the trunks each night as are coming down, the reason being that many are dropping, jumping, lowering themselves on threads, or developing wings and flying away. At higher altitudes, 'old man's beard' lichen (*Usnea* species) commonly hangs from the branches.

Growing It: In a garden or park the flowers and occasionally-red winter leaves make this tree worth planting. Most often grown from seed but can be grown from cuttings. Requires good drainage.

Pukatea

Laurelia novae-zelandiae [Family: Monimiaceae]

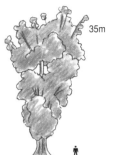

35m

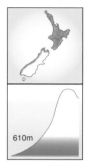

610m

Leaves:	*Opposite* (unlike beech), round even teeth, *stalks square-angled* (unlike kāmahi), dark glossy green, veins inconspicuous
Fruit:	Seed cases green, jug-shaped (late summer), releasing fluffy seeds in autumn
Trunk:	Plank-like buttresses at base
Other:	Prefers damp places

The fresh bark was steeped in hot water for neuralgia. The painkilling properties have since been proven by chemists, the leaves acting as both a local and general analgesic when chewed, while the bark contains *pukateine*, a substance with similar numbing properties to morphine but without the side effects. Pukatea was a preferred timber for Māori carving and palisade posts. Though not particularly durable in contact with the ground, the wood is lightweight and very strong, with the added advantage of being both fire-resistant and extremely hard to split. Its ability to take nails driven into it from any direction made it good planking for boats. In house-building it was used as weatherboards and external roofing and valued by cabinetmakers and woodturners for its attractive greenish-brown colouring. The link between this tree and its namesake pukatea (*Pisonia grandis*) of tropical Polynesia is not known – although both trees produce soft wood that rots readily in contact with the ground.

Nature Notes: In October and November, the inconspicuous, yellow-green flowers are visited by bellbirds and by honey bees (collecting the white pollen), but the tree is primarily wind pollinated. When the green capsules burst, wind also disperses the dandelion-like seeds. Kōkako (left) eat the leaves. Leaves are webbed together by caterpillars of the native 'blackheaded leafroller' moth. In summer and autumn, crumpled dead leaves often conceal 4 or 5 caterpillars each of the 'kawakawa looper' moth. On half-dead wood, look out for the spectacular 'giraffe weevil', the male of which can often be 7 cm long, its grubs feeding on fungi and yeast for two years in tunnels in the rotten wood until this slowly becomes riddled. A kind of 'sooty beech scale' insect feeds on the sap, using a long wax tube to exude honeydew. The tree is rarely browsed by possums and is particularly well adapted to living in damp places.

Growing It: In natural surroundings, pukatea often reaches an immense height, but in cultivation grows only slowly, remaining a manageable tree for specimen planting, growing happily in wet ground even down to the water's edge. Prefers a deep, rich soil. Raised from seed or semi-hardwood cuttings.

LEAVES OPPOSITE

17

Makomako
Wineberry

Aristotelia serrata [Family: Elaeocarpaceae]

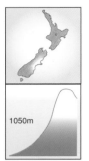
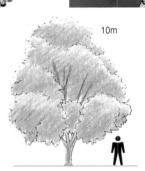

10m

Leaves:	*Opposite* (unlike houhere), deep teeth, *red stalks*, usually *reddish underneath*
Flowers:	Small and pinkish-red (late spring)
Fruit:	Small, dark red to black (on female trees only) in late summer
Other:	Common in regrowth forest. In cold areas may lose its leaves

Named after mako – related light-wooded trees [Malvales] in the tropical Pacific with similar heart-shaped leaves whose barks were also used for dye and fibre. Māori stripped sections of bark of the New Zealand tree and folded them to make simple water containers. The bark was used medicinally: soaked in cold water, the infusion used for sore eyes or boiled to make a bath for rheumatic patients. Māori also bruised the bark and steeped it in hot water to produce a blue black dye for colouring flax. As the European name suggests, the berries were subsequently used for making wine, or the fruit cooked to make jellies and jams. Māori ate these raw, their taste varying (in my experience) from sweet to decidedly bitter (if you chew the seed). Liquid from boiled leaves was applied to burns, boils, sore eyes and rheumatic pains. The reddish colouring, especially evident on young leaves, is due to *anthocyanins*, which are believed to help protect these from strong sunlight. The timber was occasionally used for fence rails, woodturning and marquetry, but its main use has been in making charcoal for the manufacture of certain kinds of gunpowder.

Nature Notes: Nectar from the pink flowers is eaten by stitchbirds; pollen by native weevils. The fruit is a favourite of tūī, bellbirds, kererū and silvereyes. Kererū also eat the leaves. Leaves are high in *phenols*, making them a favourite food of possums, especially in autumn. In the North Island, finger-sized holes in the trunk are made by the large caterpillars of the 'pūriri moth'. Also common are twig-like caterpillars of the 'forest semilooper' moth on the leaves. Dimples in young leaves are made by the young stage of the 'wineberry psyllid' insect; damage of young leaf buds by grubs of the 'wineberry gall midge'. The 'wineberry flower weevil' feeds in the male flowers. Leaves and young trees are freely eaten by goats, cattle and deer. One of the first trees to recolonise areas of forest cleared by fire.

Growing It: Attractive as a flowering specimen or background tree, providing quick, light shade for growing other plants – a function it fulfils just as well in the garden as in the natural regeneration of damaged forest. Grows easily from seed or stem cuttings and transplants easily.

Porokaiwhiri Pigeonwood

Hedycarya arborea [Family: Monimiaceae]

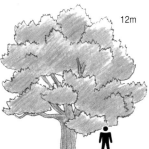

12m

800m

Leaves:	*Opposite* (unlike māhoe), dark glossy green above, paler below, *very widely-spaced teeth*
Flowers:	Small and cream, strongly sweet-smelling (in spring)
Fruit:	Orange-red in bunches (on female trees only) in late spring and early summer
Trunk:	Bark dark brown, fairly smooth
Other:	New branchlets furry brown

This tree is easily overlooked in the forest until around November when the inconspicuous flowers of male trees produce a jasmine-like fragrance. Even then, it takes a curious nose to find it. Then again, in early summer, bunches of bright orange-red fruit appear, catching the eye. Māori are not known to have eaten these fruit and indeed tests indicate that some parts of the tree could be poisonous. The fruit is, however, enjoyed in large quantities by kererū (New Zealand pigeons), hence the European name. Māori names such as porokaiwhiri, and likewise **kaiwhiri**, refer to birds flocking (whiri) to this tree in late spring and early summer to feed (kai) on the fruit. Māori used the leaves – in the 19th century at least – in vapour baths. Although few special uses of the soft, white, straight-grained wood are known, Māori did use it to make digging sticks.

Nature Notes: Even in light wind, copious pollen is shed from male flowers, suggesting that the plant is primarily wind pollinated; however, their strong scent suggests insects also play a role. Possums rarely eat the leaves but take buds and flowers, competing for fruit with kererū, tūī, kōkako, weka, blackbirds and thrushes (all of which spread the seeds) and kākā, kiore and ship rats (which chew and destroy seeds). Fruit were also eaten by huia (prior to that bird's extinction). Kōkako have been observed eating the leaves, also chewing these to feed to their chicks. Among the insects seen on the trunk are two conspicuous kinds of native beetles whose grubs tunnel into the dead wood: the spectacularly large 'giraffe weevil' (the adult male of which is typically 7 cm long) and the pretty little 'Sinclair's longhorn' (right). Leaves and young trees are freely eaten by goats and deer.

Growing It: The tree's erect shape, the fragrance of its blossoms, the bright colour and attractiveness to native birds of its fruit – all these make pigeonwood a worthwhile specimen tree, especially in larger gardens or in a park. It requires some shelter from wind and protection from frost while young, and is best planted in a good, rather deep, moist soil. If you want the tree to produce fruit, remember to plant trees of both sexes. Grows easily from seed but can also be grown from semi-hardwood cuttings.

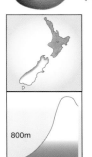

LEAVES OPPOSITE

Kohekohe

Dysoxylum spectabile [Family: Meliaceae]

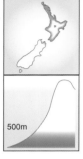

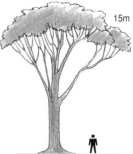

15m

500m

Leaves:	*In 3 or 4 opposite pairs*, dark and shiny
Flowers:	Long, drooping sprays, white, fragrant, growing directly from trunk or branches (early winter)
Fruit:	Round green capsule, 2.5 cm across, splitting to reveal an orange-red centre (late autumn)
Other:	*Buttress roots* at base of trunk

The origin of the name **kohe** or kohekohe (as in the place name, Pukekohe – 'the hill on which kohekohe grew') remains obscure. In the tropical Pacific, this name in various forms is widely used for Polynesian bamboo, but the link between these plants has so far eluded scholars. In Māori medicine, the astringent, orange-red pulp of the fruit was eaten by those with pulmonary tuberculosis to relieve blood-spitting. The bark and leaves were both regarded as an effective tonic, their bitter taste helping to account for their reported use as ingredients of home-made beer. Among the long list of healing properties attributed to them are the use of a gargled tea of leaves to soothe sore throats and a brew incorporating the bark for haemorrhages. Chemical analysis of the heartwood has found *catechin*, which helps control diarrhoea and throat infections. The heartwood and bark are high in tannin (effective against haemorrhaging) and also contain *ß-sitosterol*, a compound that blocks cholesterol absorption, resulting in lower blood cholesterol levels. The wood was used by Māori for canoes, later by furniture makers and for fence posts in well-drained sand, and is still highly valued by woodcarvers.

Nature Notes: At night, a sweet scent lures moths to the flowers. Tūī, korimako (bellbirds), stitchbirds, kākā and silvereyes also eat the nectar, picking up the few sticky pollen grains found here, thus helping to fertilise the flowers. The flowers themselves are eaten by kākāriki. Unfortunately, the tree is dying out in some areas due to severe browsing by possums. Possums eat the fruit, competing with kererū (New Zealand pigeons), kōkako, tūī, weka, silvereyes (shown above, eating the fruit), blackbirds, thrushes and starlings (some of which help spread the seeds), and kākā and kiore (which break up the seeds). Conspicuous insects found here include the caterpillars of two native 'leaf-tyer moths' (including the 'blackheaded leafroller') that web leaves together, also the 'giraffe weevil' and at least two kinds of native 'longhorn beetle'.

Growing It: Frost tender and needs reasonable shelter but makes a very attractive specimen tree. Grown from either seed or cuttings. Thrives only in a rich, well-drained soil.

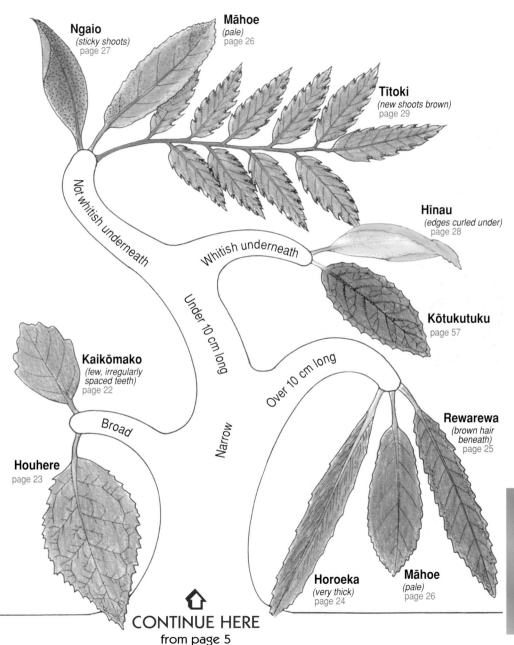

Ngaio
(sticky shoots)
page 27

Māhoe
(pale)
page 26

Tītoki
(new shoots brown)
page 29

Hīnau
(edges curled under)
page 28

Kōtukutuku
page 57

Kaikōmako
(few, irregularly spaced teeth)
page 22

Rewarewa
(brown hair beneath)
page 25

Houhere
page 23

Horoeka
(very thick)
page 24

Māhoe
(pale)
page 26

Not whitish underneath

Whitish underneath

Under 10 cm long

Over 10 cm long

Broad

Narrow

⬆
CONTINUE HERE
from page 5

LEAVES ALTERNATING

YOU CAN MEASURE YOUR LEAF HERE
— 10 cm —

Kaikōmako

Pennantia corymbosa [Family: Icacinaceae]

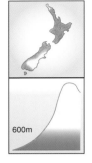

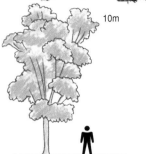

10m

600m

Leaves:	Alternating or clustered, 3–l0 cm long (smaller on young trees), *irregular widely-spaced teeth*
Flowers:	Small, 5-petalled, creamy white, fragrant and profuse (early summer)
Fruit:	Small and black (on female trees only) in early autumn
Trunk:	Grey, sometimes with sooty mould

The fruit is popular with bellbirds, explaining the Māori name, 'kai' meaning 'food', and 'kōmako' meaning 'bellbird'. Legends tell of how Māui learnt the secret of making fire from Mahuika, the goddess of fire, and that this is one of the woods he used. Kaikōmako was chosen because it is particularly hard. A thoroughly dry and sharply pointed stick of it is scraped along the grain of a dry slab of softer wood such as māhoe or patete, gradually forming a groove that fills with fine dust. This dust accumulates gradually at the end of the groove and, if the scraping is vigorous enough, will eventually start to smoke. With skill, patience and dedicated fanning or blowing, this smouldering dust will catch alight. For Polynesians generally, this was the traditional method of lighting fires. The dead twigs also make good kindling. Being hard and durable, the wood was also recommended to European settlers for chisel handles and the like. Other than this, the timber was not much used, except for an occasional, attractively marked piece chosen for woodturning or for ornamental detail in furniture-making.

Nature Notes: September to December, masses of small white flowers use the 'flag effect' to attract small pollinating insects, including honey bees. The fruit is popular with kererū, korimako or kōmako (bellbirds), tūī, whiteheads, kōkako, weka and possums. Kōkako and kererū also eat the leaves. The tree's tangled juvenile form (thought to have once given the tree protection from browsing moa), continues to provide some protection from goats, deer and cattle. The 'kaikōmako mirid' sucks the sap while the 'kaikōmako gall mite' forms tiny lumps (galls) on the leaves. Native caterpillars found here include those of the 'lawyer owlet' moth and looper caterpillars of the 'brown evening moth' (top right).

Growing It: In its slender, mature form, kaikōmako makes a good specimen tree, well-suited to small gardens. However, at the young stage, it can look quite scraggly. Grows easily from seed but semi-hardwood cuttings from the adult tree will shortcut the juvenile stage altogether and produce a flowering specimen at a younger age. Thrives only in a rich, moist soil.

Houhere
Lacebark

Hoheria populnea [Family: Malvaceae]

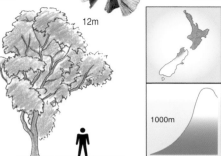

12m

1000m

Leaves:	*Alternating* (unlike makomako), 5–12 cm long, edged with large, sharp teeth
Flowers:	Large, white, star-like (late summer or autumn)
Seeds:	In winged seed capsules (mid-autumn to mid-winter)
Other:	*Young branches grooved.* The various kinds of lacebark have different-shaped leaves, but all tend to grow along forest edges

This name for fibre plants, 'houhere', is found in Rarotonga, Niue and Hawai`i. Like the European name, it refers to a 2–3 cm thick layer of lacy, matted fibres (below) that lies just beneath the outside bark of the mature tree. Māori twisted strips of this into rope or beat it to make felted bark sheets similar to tapa cloth; strips were also made into headbands and woven like straw into soft, lightweight, broad-brimmed hats. Princess Te Puea Herangi was to be seen wearing one of these regularly to the time of her death in 1952. Māori also soaked this inner bark in cold water to make a jelly used externally for sore and weak eyes and internally for soothing the digestive system. Houhere rarely grows in large, pure stands – a fact that helped save it from being exploited on a large scale for papermaking or firewood.

Nature Notes: Tūī, bellbirds, stitchbirds, native flies, thrips and honey bees visit the flowers for nectar, especially in May. The winged seed capsules are wind-borne. Leaves are a winter food for kererū (New Zealand pigeon) and, in spring, feed moth caterpillars of the 'lacebark looper' and 'patē owlet'. Summer is the best time to find a very large spiny stick insect feeding here: the so-called 'horrid stick insect'. Young leaves are mined by caterpillars of the 'lacebark leafminer moth', while finger-sized holes in the trunk are made by caterpillars of the 'pūriri moth'. The tree also supports two 'lacebark gall mites' – one forming galls on the undersides of leaves; the other producing a large, woody, brown 'lacebark gall' (top left) on stems and leaves; also grubs of several weevils (a 'lacebark fruit weevil', 'lacebark flower weevil' and 'lacebark flowerbud weevil'). The native yellow-berried mistletoe (*Ileostylis micranthus*) often perches in the branches. However, in many areas, whole trees are being eliminated by goats and deer. In winter, the leaves are also moderately palatable to possums.

Growing It: A popular garden tree. Grows well from seed (collected in May) or from semi-hardwood cuttings. Takes the occasional pruning. Requires good drainage. Relatively short-lived.

Botanists currently differentiate between *Hoheria populnea* and *Hoheria sexstylosa* (**long-leaved lacebark**).

TOOTHED

LEAVES ALTERNATING

Horoeka
Lancewood

Pseudopanax crassifolius [Family: Araliaceae]

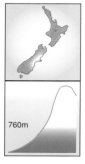

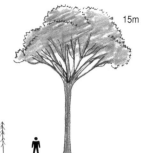

15m

760m

Leaves:	Alternating, with teeth. On young trees 30 cm (or more) long, on adult trees 7–20 cm (can be toothless), *central rib and underside pale*
Fruit:	4–5 mm, purplish-black (on female trees only) in autumn/ winter
Trunk:	Sinewy and thin like rope, especially when young

Also known as **kokoeka**, both Māori names linking it with a spindly-trunked Tahitian tree, `oro`e`a (*Cyclophyllum barbatum*) that has an equally distinctive shape and likewise provided Polynesians with a ready source of poles. The straight and often very slender, branchless stems of the New Zealand tree were sharpened by southern Māori and hardened by fire to make bird spears and this is the likely origin of the tree's European name. Similar lengths of straight, flexible, pole-like trunks were also cut for use as horse whips. As a timber, horoeka appears to have been most used in Otago. Although not as durable as some woods, piles supporting the first jetty built at Port Chalmers around 1850 lasted intact for 30 years. Horoeka is particularly striking while still young – with narrow, downward-pointing, lance-like leaves that can be over one metre long. After about twenty years – in one of the greatest transformations to take place between juvenile and adult tree – these incredibly long juvenile leaves are replaced by ones less than half their length, and around twice their width. The midribs of young leaves are surprisingly strong and pliable when fresh and were used by early forest workers as bootlaces and for mending bridles and harnesses.

Nature Notes: In late February clusters of small flowers flag the attention of pollinating insects including honey bees. The nectar is also sometimes eaten by stitchbirds. Tūī, bellbirds, kererū, whiteheads, kākā, silvereyes, weka and, in winter, even miromiro (tomtits) feed on the fruit. Rats eat the seeds. Other conspicuous insects found on the plant include the 'squeaking longhorn' beetle. (Yes, if you pick it up this will indeed often squeak.) On the leaves, look out for pits or pale dots made by the young stage of the 'lancewood psyllid' insect; also pale squiggly lines inside the leaves made by tiny caterpillars of the 'lancewood leafminer' moth as they chew their way along miniature tunnels within. Freely eaten by goats and deer, and sometimes also by possums. Deer are also known for eating the fallen leaves. The roots are a common host of the parasitic, flowering *Dactylanthus* wood rose, pua reinga.

Growing It: A popular garden tree or tub plant particularly in its juvenile stage, which it retains for 15–20 years. Grows easily from fresh, ripe seed (collected when the fruit is soft). Prefers good drainage.

Rewarewa
New Zealand Honeysuckle

Knightia excelsa [Family: Proteaceae]

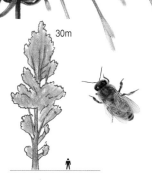

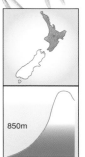

Leaves: Long, stiff, with widely spaced teeth, *undersides, mid-vein and new growth velvety brown* (seedling leaves longer)

Flowers: In clusters, velvety, brick red in bud, peeling back to reveal yellow centres (late spring)

Seeds: In long rusty brown pods (summer). Shaped like a canoe

Māori likened the shape of the open seedpods (below) to a canoe – complete with prow and stern-posts – inspiring a traditional East Coast story in which a boy (Tautini-Awhitia) takes a magical voyage seated in one. In regrowth forest the tree's poplar-like form is conspicuous, often poking up mast-like through the scrub canopy; 'rewa' means 'elevated' or the 'mast of a canoe'. Most trampers first notice this tree in late spring when its strange, velvety, red-and-yellow flowers fall on the track. To Māori the appearance of these served as a seasonal marker, signalling the sixth month of their calendar (November). Europeans named the tree for the likeness of these flowers to those of honeysuckle. Nectar from picked flowers supplied Māori with a minor source of food, collected by tapping these on the inside of a gourd vessel. The inner bark would be bandaged over a fresh wound to stem bleeding and to speed healing. European settlers put the rather dark, flecked wood to a number of decorative uses: making tables, writing desks, picture frames, stationery cases, woodturning and veneer work (like the glove box lid of my old Morris Minor). Useless as firewood, settlers nicknamed it '**bucket-of-water tree**'.

Nature Notes: Pollen from the tree has been identified on Vaseline smears placed on short-tailed bat, indicating that at night they visit the flowers, but the tree is primarily bird pollinated, with nectar being taken by tūī, korimako (bellbirds), hihi (stitchbirds), kākā, silvereyes, and introduced honey bees (which produce from it an unusually dark and rich flavoured honey). The flowers themselves are eaten by kererū (New Zealand pigeons), kōkako, kākāriki and possums. Possums, however, rarely eat the leaves. Specialist insects to look out for here include the 'rewarewa leafstalk weevil' found in the stalks of fallen leaves, and – on the underside of the leaves – the 'rewarewa felted scale' insect.

Growing It: Recommended as a specimen tree suitable for any medium-sized garden. Hardy enough to grow as far south as Invercargill (along the coast at least), tolerating wind. Will grow in very dry ground and tolerates both sun and shade but prefers a good, well-drained, friable soil and plenty of light. Easily raised from fresh seed.

TOOTHED

LEAVES ALTERNATING

Māhoe
Whiteywood

Melicytus ramiflorus [Family: Violaceae]

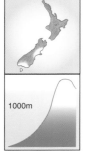

10m

Leaves:	*Alternating*, toothed
Flowers:	Small, greenish-yellow, sweet-scented, growing directly from branches (early summer)
Fruit:	Small, purple (on female trees only) in late summer
Trunk:	Smooth, *white lichen patches*
Other:	Very common in regrowth and coastal bush. Leaf skeletons very common beneath the tree

Its primary use by Māori was to generate fire by scraping a pointed stick of hard wood (kaikōmako or tōtara) on a dry māhoe slab; Europeans burnt the wood to produce charcoal for making gunpowder. In naming it, Māori were apparently cautioning novices not to use it for making paddles ('hoe' meaning 'paddle'), 'mā' meaning 'ashamed or the pale colour one turns on being ashamed', for the white wood is indeed brittle and useless. Woodturners, however, find it a useful practice wood when turned green. The frayed inner bark was applied as a pack to burns and the liquid from boiled leaves applied for rheumatism and scabies. Weavers extract a dull green dye from the leaves. An old name, **cowleaf**, refers to its use as fodder during drought, while 'whiteywood' describes both the timber colour and the white lichen patches on the trunk. Known in the South Island as **hinahina** ('hina' meaning 'pale or grey in colour').

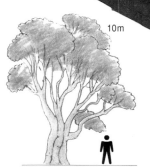

Nature Notes: Nectar collected by kākā, tūī, bellbirds, stitchbirds, flies, thrips and honey bees. Possums eat the fruit as do tūī, bellbirds, kererū, whiteheads, kākāriki, kōkako, silvereyes, weka and green geckos. Horizontal territorial bite marks on trunks are left by possums, which eat the leaves, as do kōkako, kererū and deer – also goats, which will even climb out along the branches. Fallen leaf skeletons are taken by riflemen and grey warblers as nesting material. Grubs of native 'lemon tree borer' beetles tunnel live branches; these are often taken over by tree wētā, which enlarge them over several years – hence the tree's alternative name, **kaiwētā**. Trees also support two kinds of 'māhoe flowerbud gall mite', a 'māhoe leaf-feeding flat mite', 'māhoe whitefly' (leaves white wax on leaves) and 'lesser bronze cicada' (whose nymphs feed almost exclusively on māhoe roots). Pale meandering lines in leaves are left by tiny maggots of the 'māhoe leafminer fly'. Caterpillars of the 'māhoe stripper' moth feed voraciously on leaves; while those of 'sharp-tipped bell moth' web leaves together. Ear fungus is common on the trunks. Rusty red patches on leaves (right) are a kind of *Trentepohlia* alga.

Growing It: In cultivation, māhoe is recommended for specimen planting in large gardens as fast-growing shade and for the attractiveness of female trees to birds. Does best in a sheltered position, but will tolerate wind. Grows well from seed or semi-hardwood cuttings. Can live for over 80 years.

Ngaio
Myoporum laetum [Family: Myoporaceae]

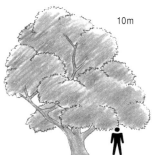

10m

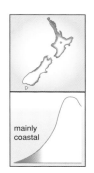

mainly coastal

Leaves: Hold a leaf up to the light to see the *pale dot-like oil glands*; note small teeth toward the tip

Flowers: Small, white, with purple spots (late spring and early summer)

Fruit: Small, reddish-purple (early autumn)

Other: *Sticky black leaf buds* (Buds of the **Australian ngaio** – often planted by mistake – are green.)

The name ngaio was brought to New Zealand from Mangaia (Southern Cook Islands), Austral Islands or Hawai`i, where closely related plants (*Myoporum*) go by the same name. Māori rubbed sticky black shoots of the New Zealand plant on skin to prevent mosquito and sandfly bites, and also sometimes ate the ripe, reddish-purple fruit. However, apart from tasting quite bitter, these fruits are best left alone since the whole plant is now known to contain a substance (*ngaione*) that is toxic to the liver. This compound does have fungicidal and bactericidal properties too, which may help explain some of the many external medicinal uses of the leaves and bark. The leaves, for example, were bruised and warmed to release their oil and used as a poultice for septic wounds – a remedy that proved sufficiently effective to be used subsequently by veterinarians on horses. Ngaio leaves were also used for making sheep dip. Indeed, recent tests have confirmed antibacterial properties against *Staphylococcus aureus* (golden staph). The main timber uses of ngaio are furniture-making and woodturning.

Nature Notes: Bellbirds, stitchbirds and native flies visit the flowers for nectar, as do honey bees, which use the sticky gum from buds in the construction of their hives. At night, the flowers are visited by Pacific geckos and moths. The fruit is eaten by kererū, tūī and kākāriki (parakeets). Conspicuous insects here include caterpillars of the 'greenheaded leafroller' moth; two 'ngaio gall mites' (causing lumps on the leaves); the 'ngaio shoot mirid' insect (on young shoots); grubs of the 'ngaio leafminer fly' (making blotch mines in leaves); and caterpillars of the 'ngaio stem gall moth' (boring into new stems, forming lumps on them). More spectacular swellings on the stems are, however, caused by the 'ngaio rust fungus'. Goats tend to avoid it yet, in spite of its toxicity to many creatures, possums still relish it.

Growing It: Planted as a shelter tree particularly near the sea where it is found naturally. Can be trimmed into a hedge plant. Given enough space, its gnarled growth and spreading head make it a good specimen tree. Frost tender when young. Usually grown from seed but is very easy to grow from cuttings too. Note that the **Australian ngaio** (*M. insulare*) is often planted by mistake – see above.

TOOTHED

LEAVES ALTERNATING

Hīnau
Elaeocarpus dentatus [Family: Elaeocarpaceae]

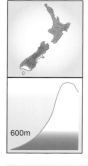

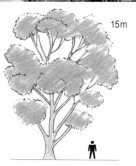

15m

600m

Leaves:	6–10 cm long, *whitish underneath*, small bumps along top surface, small teeth along *curled* edges
Flowers:	Drooping, bell-shaped, white, fragrant (late spring)
Fruit:	12 mm long, purplish when ripe (early autumn)
Trunk:	Greyish

Originally known, south of Auckland, as **whīnau**. Māori crushed and pounded the berries, then strained out and discarded the large stones (which are very hard and totally inedible) to obtain the soft, thin flesh, which were greatly valued as food, and shaped into pudding-like cakes. Though rarely eaten nowadays, these cakes (pōhā or pōwhā) were cooked hāngi-style for two hours or more, then offered as a welcome to honoured guests. ('Whī-nau' means 'can come'). Tūhoe Māori noted the blooming of hīnau as a seasonal marker (in late spring) for when best to burn off bracken fern fronds to improve the crop to be obtained from the fern's edible roots. A black pigment for tattooing was made from an exudation taken from the tree, while the bark combined with a black mud mordant provided a black dye for colouring flax. With an average tannin content of over 7 percent, the bark became an important raw material in the mid-19th century for a local leather tanning industry and was subsequently used by weavers as a greenish dye. Children have even used this bark to make a writing ink. Māori folded sheets of this bark into simple water containers too and used the bark medicinally (or rather a decoction of it in a hot bath) as a cure for skin diseases.

Nature Notes: October to November, kākā, tūī, korimako (bellbirds), hihi (stitchbirds) and honey bees collect the nectar. Fruit was eaten by the now-extinct huia, but is now dispersed by brown kiwi, weka, kererū (New Zealand pigeon) and kōkako. Kākā and rats destroy the seeds. Possums do not usually eat the leaves, but do eat large quantities of buds and fruit, contributing to the animal's reproductive success. Wild pigs likewise eat the fruit. Conspicuous insects here include the 'acutewinged click beetle'. On summer nights, wētā are also seen climbing the trunk. The leaves are sometimes mined by the caterpillar of a native leafminer moth (which will also fold the tips of young leaves). Freely eaten by goats and deer.

Growing It: Bell-shaped flowers make hīnau an attractive garden tree; however, it is very slow growing, taking several years to flower. Best planted in a good deep soil with shelter from wind. Seed can be very slow and hard to germinate.

Tītoki
Alectryon excelsus [Family: Sapindaceae]

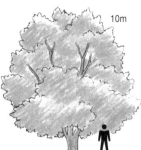

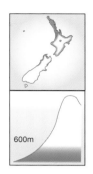

Leaves: Alternating to almost opposite, *in 4–6 pairs*, mostly without teeth, *new growth with brown fur*

Fruit: Hard, brown seed case, splits to reveal large shiny black seed in juicy red pulp (on female trees only) in early summer

Other: Most common on river flats

Also known as **tokitoki**, 'toki' meaning 'axe', an element found in several indigenous names of hard-wooded trees of the tropical Pacific. It is indeed hard and particularly suitable for axe handles – a fact that also inspired the old European name, **New Zealand ash**. For its strength and elasticity, the timber was also prized by wheelwrights and coach-makers. Māori occasionally ate the pulp of the fruit, but the real value lay in the oil from the large, shiny black seed, explaining why tītoki was one of the few trees traditionally planted by Māori. These seeds were crushed with a tourniquet-style flax (or supplejack) bag to extract a greenish oil. This served as a hair oil in which leaves or gums would be steeped to add fragrance. When Captain Jean-Francois de Surville's ship, the *St Jean Baptiste*, visited these shores in 1769–1770, the crew purchased tītoki oil from local Māori for lighting their ship. Later this oil was recommended as a fine-grade lubricant suitable for use by watchmakers. Medicinally, the oil was usually applied externally for soothing and healing purposes. Recent laboratory research (1995) revealed that an extract of the leaves and twigs possesses antiviral properties, effective against influenza type A. Since the 1970s, the fruit has been an ingredient of a commercial liqueur.

Nature Notes: The inconspicuous flowers appear in clusters, flagging the attention of small pollinating insects to collect a meagre supply of sticky pollen grains. The fruit is eaten, and seeds spread, by kererū, tūī, kōkako, blackbirds and thrushes. Conspicuous insects here in summer include the native 'lemon tree borer' beetle and a small, unique bronze beetle (5 mm) which chews shot-like holes in the leaves. Caterpillars of a slender, black-and-white 'tītoki cocoon-weaver' moth chew out the inside of leaves, while tiny caterpillars of the 'tītoki fruit borer' moth live inside the capsules, where they damage the seed. A kind of lichen is common on the leaves. Possums are strongly attracted to the fruit and leaves, which they eat freely. To a lesser extent, trees are also browsed by deer.

Growing It: Sensitive to frost and wind, but makes a good specimen or shade tree. Easiest to grow from seed taken from mature capsules. Needs a well-drained soil and some shelter from wind.

TOOTHED

LEAVES ALTERNATING

Tānekaha
Celery Pine

Phyllocladus trichomanoides [Family: Phyllocladaceae]

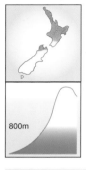

20m

800m

Leaves:	1.5–2.5 cm long, fan-like and leathery, *together looking like a celery leaf* *
Trunk:	Smooth with grey patches
Other:	*Often quite symmetrical with branches in regular tiers.* (A more northern **toatoa** has larger 'leaves'. The leaves of the more southern and high country **mountain toatoa** are smaller.)

Māori name tāne-kaha (strong man) refers to the fact that the wood was prized by Māori warriors for making double-pointed fighting spears (koikoi). An alternative name, **toatoa** (used for all members of the genus) is also derived from warrior ('toa'), a name coined in tropical Polynesia for the spear-making ironwood (*Casuarina equisetifolia*). Sapling tānekaha subsequently supplied London with straight, flexible rods to make walking sticks. Its remarkable flexibility made it suitable too for fishing rods. The timber was used for the manufacture of threshing machines, mine props and fish hooks. The bark was pounded by Māori to a pulp in cold water. Soaking flax garments and mats in it, they brought this mixture to the boil by throwing in hot stones to produce a red-brown dye. Homespinners used this bark in a similar way for dyeing wool. The bark was also a remedy for dysentery (most likely due to its exceptionally high tannin content) and ingeniously folded into simple water containers. Large quantities of tānekaha bark were exported to Germany in the late 19th century, as a source of red and pink dyes and to London for use as an organic mordant in the manufacture of kid gloves.

Nature Notes: The flowers and 'leaves' are eaten by kererū (New Zealand pigeons). The 'leaves' contain *ecdysone*, which acts as an insecticide by interfering with hormones governing the moulting of insects. Nevertheless, several conspicuous insects do feed on it, including the 'pallid longhorn' beetle and two other native longhorn beetles; also the specialist caterpillars of both the 'celery pine looper' (*Pseudocoremia monacha*) moth (top), and 'tānekaha leafroller' (*Catamacta alopecana*) moth (left), which web leaves together; and a couple of kinds of native 'catkin weevils' whose grubs and adults feed in the pollen cones. Small, brown, waxy lumps on the underside of 'leaves' are made by the 'tānekaha scale' insect. Generally avoided by deer, goats etc.

Growing It: In cultivation, it forms an attractively symmetrical specimen tree and is fairly fast-growing. Hard to propagate from cuttings, and only slightly easier from fresh seed. Needs a well-drained soil.

* To the layperson, these look like leaves, but technically are, in fact, a flattened stem.

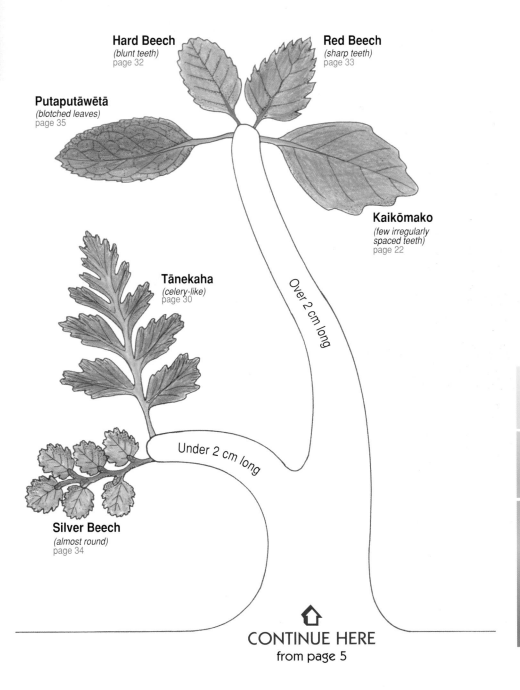

Hard Beech
(blunt teeth)
page 32

Red Beech
(sharp teeth)
page 33

Putaputāwētā
(blotched leaves)
page 35

Kaikōmako
*(few irregularly
spaced teeth)*
page 22

Tānekaha
(celery-like)
page 30

Over 2 cm long

Under 2 cm long

Silver Beech
(almost round)
page 34

⬆
CONTINUE HERE
from page 5

YOU CAN MEASURE YOUR LEAF HERE   ├── 2 cm ──┤

Tawhai Raunui
Hard Beech

Nothofagus truncata [Family: Nothofagaceae]

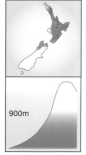

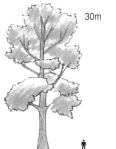

30m

900m

Leaves:	*Alternating* (unlike kāmahi), 2.5–4 cm long with blunt teeth (unlike red beech). *Four or more* veins each side of central vein (unlike silver beech). Loses many of its leaves in early spring
Trunk:	Often buttressed at base, bark thick, furrowed, grey

Hard beech and red beech are very similar. Not only do they share the same Māori name (meaning 'large-leaved beech'), but early botanists believed them to be the same tree. The only sure way to tell them apart is to look on the underside of a leaf. If you find one or more small, furry, light brown spots where the first side veins meet the central vein of the leaf, then it is a red beech. If not, it is a hard beech. The timber of hard beech was highly thought of in the late 19th century for railway sleepers, marine piles, mine props and – in housebuilding – for piles, framing, floor joists and weatherboards. Of the native beeches, its timber is the most durable and is, as the name suggests, the hardest. Unfortunately, the silica in the wood rays also has a drastic blunting effect on saws, chisels and power tools, making it an unpopular wood for turning and furniture-making. Like the timber of other native beeches, hard beech is not known to have had a specific Māori use.

Nature Notes: Wind pollinated. Kererū (pigeons) eat the leaves and tiny flowers. Mice eat fallen seeds, leading in heavy seeding years to mice plagues. Kākāriki (native parakeets) eat leaf buds, flowerbuds, flowers and seeds. Among the invertebrates found on it are the 'beech buprestid' beetle (right) and 'hard beech leafminer weevil', the caterpillars of a 'beech gall moth', four types of 'native beech mite', two 'native beech mealybugs', two 'native beech scale insects' and a 'native beech aphid'. Honeydew is sometimes found on the end of fine tubes of 'sooty beech scale' insects on the trunk; this attracts various birds, lizards and insects (including bees and wasps) and provides food for a sooty mould. On summer nights, one can see 'Helms' beech weevil' and ground wētā climbing the trunks. Indeed, four times as many insects of all sorts have been observed climbing the trunk each night as are coming down. The rest drop, jump, lower themselves on threads or develop wings and fly away.

Growing It: Hard beech is the only native beech commonly found growing north of Auckland. A handsome tree, suitable for specimen planting where there is space, it grows easily from seed (collected in summer), provided the seed is fresh. Will not tolerate high winds or drought.

Tawhai Raunui
Red Beech

Nothofagus fusca [Family: Nothofagaceae]

30m

1000m

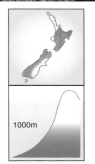

Leaves:	*Alternating* (unlike kāmahi), 2.5–4 cm long, large *sharp* teeth (unlike other beech), bright red on young trees in winter, undersides with a *furry yellowish spot* where the first side vein meets the central vein. Sheds its leaves every year.
Trunk:	Often buttressed, mostly smooth

Red beech is named after the colour of the wood, but when the leaves of young trees are shed in winter these also turn conspicuously red. This is the dominant tree across large stretches of South Island forest, forming attractive avenues along some roads in Fiordland and Nelson Province. The only specific use of the tree by Māori appears to have been as a source of black dye used for colouring flax and cabbage tree leaves. The bark was used by European settlers for tanning leather. Honeydew found on the trunks is an important winter bee food (see below); a good quality honey from this source is harvested for export. As a timber tree, red beech has been put to much the same uses as hard beech – railway sleepers, mine props, house construction, wharves and bridges. Sawn timber is particularly slow to dry, but when properly dried it was used for boatbuilding and making furniture.

Nature Notes: Wind pollinated. Seeds eaten by mice, leading in heavy seeding years to mice plagues. A sap-sucking scale insect on the trunk excretes a sweet, honeydew that feeds kākā, tūī, bellbirds, lizards, wasps, bees and a soot-like mould (which is in turn eaten by fungus beetles). Pūriri moth caterpillars tunnel into young trees, close to the ground. Caterpillars of the 'beech case moth' (*Thiotricha tetraphala*) often strip last-season's leaves; those of 'lesser beech leafroller' moth strip flowers and new leaves; the 'beech buprestid' beetle eats leaves too; while caterpillars of a 'beech stem gall moth' live in galls on twigs. The tree supports at least eight kinds of 'native beech mite', six 'native beech scale' insects, five 'native beech mealybugs', a 'native beech aphid', a 'red beech gall midge', a 'red beech deadwood weevil', a 'pinhole beech borer weevil' and a native 'beech wood wasp'. A spongy, hoof-shaped 'beech bracket fungus' and honeycomb lichen are seen on the trunks, clusters of 'red beech toadstool' on decayed wood and, dangling from branches, 'old man's beard' lichen (*Usnea* species).

Growing It: In cultivation, this is the most versatile of the native beeches, particularly as a specimen tree in parks and large lawns. Can be clipped as a hedge or shelter tree or grown in a container. Grows readily from seed (collected in summer) – so long as the seed is fresh.

SMALL

TOOTHED

LEAVES ALTERNATING

33

Tawhai
Silver Beech

Nothofagus menziesii [Family: Nothofagaceae]

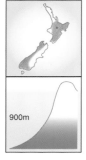

30m

900m

Leaves:	*Roundish*, 8–12 mm (unlike other beech), with *rounded double teeth*
Trunk:	Often buttressed, bark of young trees has horizontal cracks; bark of older trees rough and flaking
Other:	Young shoots covered in brown hairs

'Tavai' is a Polynesian name for a tropical timber tree *Rhus taitensis*, that provides a locally important source of black dye. The bark of its New Zealand namesake, **tawai** or tawhai, was likewise used by Māori to produce a black dye for colouring flax and cabbage tree leaves. Named after the silvery bark of young trees, silver beech became a principal source of bark for at least one commercial leather tannery and supplied one of New Zealand's better woods for steam-bending, used by coopers to make tubs, baskets and wine casks. For its attractive grain and colouring, the wood was in steady demand around the turn of the 19th century for indoor use making 'French bedsteads' and sideboards; it remains a popular woodturning timber.

Nature Notes: Wind pollinated. Kererū eat flowers and leaves. Seeds eaten by mice or sucked by the 'native beech seed bug'. Leaves chewed by caterpillars of several 'silver beech owlet' moths, also the 'silver beech spindle' moth (*Tatosoma fasciata*) and 'silver beech flash' moth (*Pseudocoremia fluminea*), 'lesser beech leafroller' and 'mountain beech moth'; and mined by caterpillars of two 'silver beech leafminer moths' and grubs of two 'silver beech leafminer weevils' – one in a stem mine, the other in leaves. 'Pūriri moth' caterpillars are frequently extracted from trunks of North Island trees by kākā. The 'beech buprestid' beetle (below right) also eats the leaves, while adults and grubs of the 'Helms' beech weevil' are found in dead wood (also on Podocarps). The tree supports seven 'native beech gall mites' (one causing 'witches' broom' – an abnormal, tight brown clumping on growing tips); three 'native beech weevils', two 'silver beech whitefly', four 'native beech scales', six 'native beech mealybugs', a 'silver beech gall midge' and a 'native beech thrips'. A parasitic red-flowered mistletoe (*Peraxilla colensoi*) is common on stems, alongside three kinds of 'beech strawberry' (top), the most striking of which is a round, orange, honeycombed fungus about 3 cm across (itself eaten by kererū). Seedlings often eaten out by goats.

Growing It: Seldom planted, but makes an appealing specimen tree, especially while young. Can also be grown in decorative containers for patios and decks. Unlike other beeches, it doesn't shed large quantities of leaves in winter or spring. Grows easily from fresh seed (best collected in late summer).

Putaputāwētā
Marbleleaf

Carpodetus serratus [Family: Grossulariaceae]

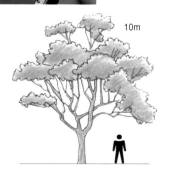

10m

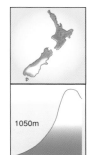

1050m

Leaves: Small, with sharp teeth, *yellowish blotches between veins*

Flowers: Small, star-like, white, in clusters, with a sweet scent (early summer)

Fruit: Round, small, black capsule (early autumn)

Other: When still young, forms a tangled shrub with much smaller leaves on zigzag branches

The Māori name (putaputa-a-wētā or 'full of wētā holes') refers to finger-sized holes in the trunks of North Island trees, which have been tunnelled by caterpillars of the giant green 'pūriri moth'. Once abandoned, these holes are often inhabited by wētā. No traditional Māori use of the tree is recorded. However, tool handles seem likely since the wood is strong, tough and elastic and was valued for this purpose by European settlers, also for fence rails and furniture. The wood is generally too sappy to be useful as firewood, eliciting the bushman's nickname, **bucket-of-water tree** (a name shared with rewarewa and kōtukutuku). Homespinners used the ripe, black fruit for colouring wool a soft green.

Nature Notes: Clusters of small white flowers flag the attention of native bees. Possums do not generally eat the leaves but do compete with bellbirds, kōkako and tauhou (silvereyes) for fruit. The tangled form and small leaves of young trees may have protected the tree from being eaten by moa, but the fruit is also known to have been eaten by them. (They probably helped distribute its seeds). Fruit and leaves are also eaten by kererū (New Zealand pigeon). North Island tree trunks are usually riddled with finger-sized holes made by caterpillars of the 'pūriri moth' (see page 8). When so occupied, the hole is capped with webbing. Only when the moth emerges and flies away six years later, does the hole provide a home to a wētā or tunnelweb spider. Twig-like caterpillars of the 'forest semilooper' moth (*Declana floccosa*) are found on the leaves. Among other invertebrates supported by the tree are three kinds of 'putaputāwētā gall mite', a 'putaputāwētā leaf-feeding flat mite', and a 'putaputāwētā gall midge'. Branches of South Island trees are also home to a parasitic white-berried native mistletoe called tāpia (*Tupeia antarctica*). Young trees are eaten by goats and deer.

Growing It: In a shrub border or as a specimen or small canopy tree, this provides moderate shelter and shade for other plants. Prefers a good, deep soil. Easily grown from ripe seed (collected when the fruit is soft), though semi-hardwood cuttings from the adult tree shortcut the scraggly juvenile stage.

SMALL

TOOTHED

LEAVES ALTERNATING

Kōwhai

Sophora microphylla [Family: Fabaceae]

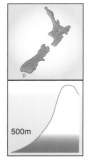
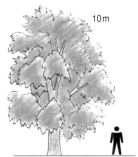

10m

500m

Leaves:	Small, round, in *20–40 pairs*, (another kōwhai has fewer, longer leaves), loses most of its leaves in winter
Flowers:	Large, drooping, bright yellow (early spring)
Seeds:	In a long brown pea-like pod (winter)
Other:	Shoots and branchlets furry brown

'Kōwhai' is a term used over much of tropical Polynesia for similar pod-bearing plants. Only in New Zealand, however, are kōwhai flowers yellow, inspiring the modern Māori word for that colour. Such striking flowers quickly attracted the attention of European horticulturists, and in 1783 kōwhai became one of the first New Zealand plants to appear in London plant catalogues. However, even without the aid of people, the plant can traverse great distances, its seeds staying afloat and viable in seawater, explaining why it grows naturally also in Chile and on distant Gough Island in the South Atlantic. Its flowering in New Zealand marked the time for some tribes to plant kūmara. The bark, inner bark, flowers, leaves and juice of the roots were all used medicinally (although experimentation is not recommended on account of the toxic alkaloids in all parts of the tree). Māori used the timber for making fern-root beaters, mauls, weapons and the blades of spades. Its strength, durability and elasticity led to a range of European uses too, including axe handles and the teeth and bows of old-style hay rakes. Bows of wood a mere 6 mm in diameter could be bent into a 23 cm semicircle without any sign of giving way. Home weavers have collected the petals to obtain a yellow dye.

Nature Notes: In the spring moonlight, moths visit the flowers. By day, the nectar attracts tūī (the primary pollinators), bellbirds, kākā, silvereyes, chaffinches, sparrows, butterflies, bumble bees and honey bees (and in Chile, hummingbirds). Kererū (pigeons) consume leaves and petals. Several specialist caterpillars feed on it. In particular, one spotted caterpillar turns into the 'kōwhai moth' (a kind of snout moth, above left), which flies in hot sunshine. The tree also supports a 'kōwhai owlet' moth, a 'kōwhai gall midge' and 'kōwhai bark weevil'. Stems and seed pods in the crown of the tree are sometimes distorted and swollen by a 'kōwhai witches' broom' rust fungus. As with other members of the pea family, kōwhai carries nitrogen-fixing root nodules, which help to improve the fertility of the soil.

Growing It: Grows easily from fresh seed or semi-hardwood cuttings. Chip old seeds first with a knife or cover with boiling water and soak overnight. Fairly fast-growing and wind tolerant.

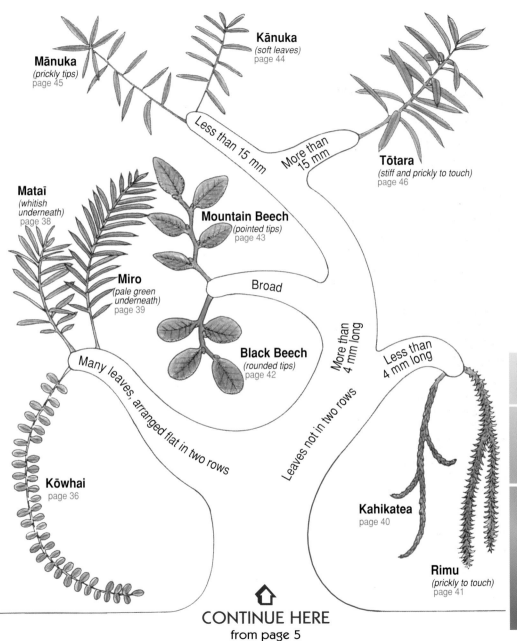

Mānuka
(prickly tips)
page 45

Kānuka
(soft leaves)
page 44

Less than 15 mm

More than 15 mm

Tōtara
(stiff and prickly to touch)
page 46

Mataī
(whitish underneath)
page 38

Mountain Beech
(pointed tips)
page 43

Miro
(pale green underneath)
page 39

Broad

Black Beech
(rounded tips)
page 42

More than 4 mm long

Less than 4 mm long

Many leaves, arranged flat in two rows

Leaves not in two rows

Kōwhai
page 36

Kahikatea
page 40

Rimu
(prickly to touch)
page 41

⌂
CONTINUE HERE
from page 5

SMALL

UNTOOTHED

LEAVES ALTERNATING

YOU CAN MEASURE YOUR LEAF HERE 4 mm |—|

Matāī

Prumnopitys taxifolia [Family: Podocarpaceae]

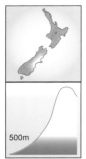
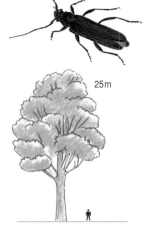

25m

500m

Leaves:	Arranged in two rows (unlike tōtara), slightly scraggly, *bluish-white underneath* (unlike miro), over 1 cm long (unlike young kahikatea), with a strong smell when crushed
Fruit:	Blue-black, round (on female trees only) in summer
Trunk:	Hammer marked on mature trees

Before felling matāī for timber, bushmen drilled the base of standing trunks with an auger to collect a sap called matāī beer. The hole was then plugged and tapped like a barrel. Taken at the right stage, the drink could be sweet and refreshing with a bitter aftertaste, and was considered effective against pulmonary tuberculosis. The Māori names, matāī or **māī** apparently refer to the sour or fermented taste (ī or māī) of this when obtained from old trees, and likewise of the raw or unripe fruit (mata). These fruits were indeed eaten raw by Māori; though the texture is slimy, they taste sweet when ripe. (The name is not to be confused with 'mātai', the Polynesian term for a 'leader or expert'.) Matāī timber was used for Māori carving, building, garden tools, musical instruments, including flutes and reed trumpets (pūkāea), and for making a type of large war gong. Previously known to Europeans as **black pine**, its strength, durability and hardwearing and non-dent properties made it suitable for the floors of public buildings. Small quantities are still sometimes used for furniture and woodturning. The bark has a relatively low tannin content but was occasionally used by leather tanneries, and to produce a brown dye for colouring wool. The wood contains *matairesinol*, which has proven effective in reducing cancer in mice.

Nature Notes: From October to November, honey bees collect pollen from the small, yellow catkins. The fruit is popular with kākā (which destroy the seeds), and tūī, kōkako, weka, blackbirds and thrushes, but seed distribution is primarily by kererū and previously by moa. Seeds are also eaten by ship rats and the outside flesh by caterpillars of the 'matāī snoutlet' moth. Kōkako eat the leaves. However, a hormonal insecticide in the leaves seems to deter all but the 'matāī leaf-tyer' caterpillar that makes its messy nest here. Maggots of two 'matāī gall flies' cause lumps in buds. Other insects include three 'matāī scale' insects, and – on dead and dying trees – 'giraffe weevils' and longhorn beetles including the 'two-toothed longhorn'. A kind of lichen is often found growing on the leaves.

Growing It: Grown from ripe seed (though slow to germinate). Cuttings taken from an adult tree will circumvent the scraggly juvenile stage. Wind tolerant. Slow-growing.

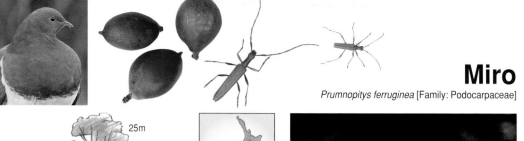

Miro

Prumnopitys ferruginea [Family: Podocarpaceae]

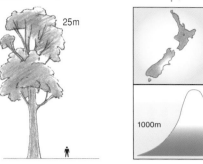

25m

1000m

Leaves:	Arranged in 2 rows (unlike tōtara), *curved, pale green below* (unlike mataī), over 1.5 cm long (unlike young kahikatea), with a strong smell when crushed
Fruit:	2 cm long, pinkish-purple (on female trees only) throughout the year
Trunk:	Hammer marked on mature trees

Also known on the East Cape as **toromiro** – both names linking this tree with carving woods of the tropical Pacific. 'Miro' means 'to twist', for the bark of the tropical miro (Pacific rosewood) was stripped and twisted or plied as a rope-like fibre. The fruit of the New Zealand miro was placed in a tourniquet-style bag and twisted by Māori to squeeze out an aromatic oil used as a body perfume, insecticide or taken internally to reduce fevers. The ripe fruit was also eaten raw and tastes sweet, but with a strong piney taste and smell. Māori relish(ed) the flavour these gave feeding kererū (New Zealand pigeon). A gum from the bark was used on wounds to stop bleeding and to heal ulcers; an infusion of leaves and bark for gonorrhoea; and an infusion of bark for stomach-ache. Folded sheets of the bark provided water containers. European settlers called the timber **brown pine**, valuing it as one the strongest of the native pines, used for marine piling and house framing, floors and weatherboards; it is not durable in contact with the ground, but is still used in small quantities for furniture, woodturning and carving.

Nature Notes: In September and October, a 'native catkin weevil' is sometimes found in the yellow catkins, feeding on pollen; honey bees collect this to take back to their hive. Kererū (New Zealand pigeons), brown kiwi, weka, kōkako – and possibly lizards – help spread the large seeds. The fruit is also a favourite – especially in autumn and early winter – with kākā and kākāpō (which chew and destroy seeds). Ship rats eat the kernels too, but leave the flesh. Kererū have also been observed eating the leaves. Conspicuous insects include 'Sinclair's longhorn' (top right) and 'pallid longhorn' beetles; caterpillars of the 'miro leafminer moth' (which mine leaves lengthwise before moving on to the next leaf); caterpillars of the 'miro litter moth' (which live on the underside of live twigs); maggots of three 'miro gall flies' (which cause large galls on buds); and a 'miro scale' insect. Though rarely eaten by goats or deer, can be heavily browsed some years by possums.

Growing It: Attractive for specimen planting. Can be clipped into a slow-growing hedge. Grown from seed or cuttings, though seeds can take up to two years to germinate. Needs reasonably good soil.

LEAVES ALTERNATING UNTOOTHED SMALL

Kahikatea

Dacrycarpus dacrydioides [Family: Podocarpaceae]

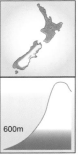

50m

600m

Leaves:	Scale-like, overlapping (in 2 rows on young growth), *soft to touch* (unlike rimu)
Fruit:	Black seed on a juicy orange-red base (on female trees only) in autumn
Trunk:	With paint-like bands when young, later grey and flaking
Other:	Common in swampy forest; young branches tend to turn upwards at the tip

A chiefly tree by any standards, this is New Zealand's tallest native tree, some over 500 years old. Pollen remains dating back over 100 million years make it also the country's most geologically ancient. It can be so thickly covered in fruit that Māori named it after the Malay apple (kahika), adding 'tea' (white) for the wood colour. The edible part is the juicy, orange-red base that holds the seed; it tastes sweet with a slight piney taste. At one feast, 60 baskets of the fruit (**koroī**) were served along with 136 pigs. Soot from burnt heartwood provided a pigment for tattooing, and resinous heartwood made bird spears, spinning tops, hair combs, fern root beaters, adze handles and canoes. Chips of wood were steeped in boiling water and the liquid drunk as a tonic; the tree contains *podocarpic* acid, which has since been shown to encourage the flow of bile. The timber (**white pine**) is odourless, clean-looking and lightweight, making it the ideal material for packing butter which is how, from 1885 to the 1940s, the vast majority of the kahikatea stands left these shores – as packaging for 56 lb slabs of butter.

Nature Notes: In spring, a 'native catkin weevil' and honey bees feed in the tiny pollen cones. Fruit popular with possums, kererū, tūī, bellbirds, kākā, kākāriki, kōkako, kiwi, silvereyes, thrushes and previously with huia. Seeds (which strongly reflect UV light rendering them more visible to some animals) are eaten by ship rats. Common on leaves and trunks of young trees are paint-like lichen, while 'old man's beard' lichen often hangs from the branches. A single mature specimen in Westland climbed in 2001 had in its branches, among the mosses and lichens, 49 seed plant and fern species – a New Zealand record. Specialist caterpillars include those of the 'kahikatea leafroller' moth. New Zealand's largest stag beetle, the 'Helms' stag beetle' is sometimes found at the base of trees, feeding on sap. In spite of a hormonal insecticide in the leaves, two 'podocarp mirids' (sucking insects), two 'podocarp scale' insects and a 'podocarp mealybug' feed here too. Huhu grubs (see page 41) tunnel into dead wood.

Growing It: A fine specimen tree in good soil, especially in wet or swampy areas. Grows easily and quickly from seed, but cuttings from mature trees will shortcut the less attractive juvenile stage.

Rimu

Dacrydium cupressinum [Family: Podocarpaceae]

35m

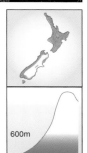

600m

Leaves:	Scale-like, overlapping, *prickly to touch* (unlike kahikatea)
Fruit:	Black seed in juicy red cup – though not common – (on female trees only), mostly in autumn
Trunk:	Dark brown, peeling in large flakes
Other:	Branches gracefully weeping

Another chiefly tree, its Māori name likens the foliage to a common seaweed of tropical Polynesia. Māori split the resinous heartwood into shreds, tying it in bundles to burn as a torch. The juicy red cup that holds the seed was eaten and the inner bark pulped to apply to burns. The bitter gum was also used to stem bleeding and the leaves used on sores. Modern chemical analysis has added a new use: *podocarpic* acid found in the heartwood can increase the flow of bile. Captain Cook used young branches to make a popular, and apparently healthy, beer: boil young rimu and mānuka branches for 3–4 hours, he says, strain and add molasses (10 gallons of it if, like him, you are brewing 240 gallons), bring to the boil, add an equal quantity of cold water, leave to cool and add yeast. The European name **red pine** describes the wood colour. Māori used it to make fern-root beaters, adze handles, canoes and bowls. It later became a major building timber and is still used for furniture, carving and woodturning. Its bark was a source of tannin for tanning leather, used by homespinners to make a brown dye. The red colouring of new growth is due to *anthocyanins* that effectively protect it from 'sunburn'.

Nature Notes: The fruit is an important food of kākāpō; it is also eaten by tūī, bellbirds, whiteheads, weka, kōkako and kererū, and the seeds by tree wētā, mice and ship rats. Birds such as saddlebacks collect twigs as nesting material. Kōkako eat the leaves, which are high in tannins and *terpenes*, thus deterring possums. Conspicuous insects include the 'prickly stick insect' (feeding on leaves) and fat edible 'huhu grubs' in dead wood (become 'huhu beetles'). Specialist insects include a 'podocarp mealybug', a 'podocarp scale', a 'rimu scale', two 'native catkin weevils', two 'podocarp weevils', a 'rimu weevil' and caterpillars of the 'rimu leaf-tyer' moth. Among moss on the trunks is a kind of 'honey mushroom' and among the many perching plants, roosting sites for short-tailed bats. Rarely eaten by goats or deer.

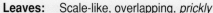

Growing It: A graceful garden tree, preferring a moist, deep soil and some shelter from wind. Usually grown from seed but also from erect-growing, semi-hardwood cuttings. Slow to germinate and slow growing too. Difficult to transplant beyond seedling stage.

Tawhai Rauriki
Black Beech

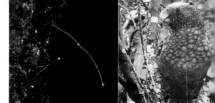

Nothofagus solandri [Family: Nothofagaceae]

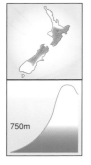

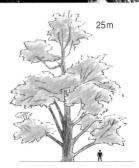

25m

750m

Leaves:	*Rounded tip* (unlike mountain beech), *no teeth* (unlike red, hard and silver beech), 1–1.5 cm long
Flowers:	Tiny, yet giving the tree a distinct reddish colour in spring
Trunk:	Bark pale and smooth on young trees, black and furrowed on old trees

Named after the dark bark, which is often blackened by a sooty mould. Black beech forests of northeastern South Island supply Canterbury beekeepers with a prized export: 'honeydew' honey. (See Nature Notes below for details on how this 'honeydew' honey is produced.) In the 19th century, the bark was collected for its high tannin content, and crushed along with bark of silver beech to make a brew for tanning leather. Black beech timber was widely used for railway sleepers, gateposts, fence rails and cartwheel spokes, and was once the major building material in Canterbury for bridges, beams and decking, flooring and wall panelling. Though stable enough when dry for use in furniture-making and wood-turning, the large quantities of silica it contains quickly blunts tools. *Nothofagus* ('false beech') trees are found in Australia, New Caledonia, New Guinea and South America, and are hence known as 'southern beech'. The New Zealand species are all found only in New Zealand.

Nature Notes: Wind pollinated. Mice eat the seeds, while 'native beech seed bugs' suck them. In northern South Island, the 'sooty beech scale' insect sucks the sap, excreting a sticky honeydew from a fine tube – food for wasps, butterflies, bees, tūī, bellbirds, kākā, kea, silvereyes, possums and a soot-like mould that often covers the trunks of trees. Conspicuous beetles here include the 'Helms' beech weevil', 'elephant weevil' and 'beech buprestid' beetle. Caterpillars include those of the 'lesser beech leafroller' moth and 'mountain beech moth'. Stem galls on twigs are inhabited by caterpillars of the 'native beech gall moth'; other galls by two 'black beech gall flies' and four 'native beech gall mites'. Alongside many non-specialist invertebrates, the tree also supports a 'black beech mirid', a 'black beech leafminer weevil', seven 'native beech mealybugs', four 'native beech scale' insects, a 'beech pinhole borer weevil', a 'native beech thrips' and a 'native beech spider mite'. Branches will sometimes host the native red mistletoe (*Peraxilla tetrapetala*) and yellow mistletoe (*Alepis flavida*).

Growing It: Where space allows, black beech can make an attractive specimen tree, with the advantage over most other beeches of being more resistant to wind damage. Like all native beeches, it prefers a well-drained soil. Grows well from fresh seed (collected in late summer).

Tawhai Rauriki
Mountain Beech

Nothofagus solandri var. *cliffortioides* [Family: Nothofagaceae]

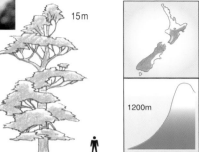

15m

1200m

Leaves: *Triangular, pointed* (unlike black beech), edges *curled under* (unlike black beech), *no teeth* (unlike red, hard and silver beech), about 1 cm long, a few hairs on top surface

Trunk: Smooth and dark

This tree is very similar to black beech and is so closely related to it that the two trees frequently hybridise. It is not surprising, then, that the Māori name does not distinguish between them; both are simply small-leaved (rauriki) beeches (tawhai). Although mountain beech is capable of growing in the most severe conditions, high in the mountains, in the south it also grows right down to sea level. Like black beech, mountain beech also provides the sought-after beech honeydew, collected by South Island beekeepers for export to Europe. The timber was widely used for making gates, fences and floors. This fact and the fact that it is not as durable as black beech has probably saved much steep country from the severe erosion and flooding that would have resulted from its removal from rugged terrain. Indeed, soil conservation in high country is without doubt the tree's most important 'use'.

Nature Notes: Wind pollinated. Seeds are eaten by mice and sucked by a 'native beech seed bug'. The sap-sucking 'sooty beech scale' insect excretes honeydew on the tree – food for tūī, kākā, kea, silvereyes, korimako (bellbirds), butterflies, bees and wasps and for a soot-like mould which is, in turn, food of fungus beetles. In winter, kākā will also strip bark to get at the sap. Two native mistletoes, common in the branches, attract tūī and bellbirds in summer. Conspicuous beetles include the 'Helms' beech weevil', 'elephant weevil' (top) and 'beech buprestid' beetle (right). Caterpillars include those of the 'mountain beech moth' (which can strip trees), and 'lesser beech leafroller' moth. Stem galls on twigs are inhabited by caterpillars of the 'native beech gall moth'; and other galls by two 'black beech gall flies' and four 'native beech gall mites'. Other specialist invertebrates here include a 'native beech mirid', a 'black beech leafminer weevil', seven 'native beech mealybugs', four 'native beech scale' insects, a 'beech pinhole borer weevil', a 'native beech thrips' and a 'native beech spider mite'. Browsed by deer. Branches will sometimes host the native red mistletoe (*Peraxilla tetrapetala*) and yellow mistletoe (*Alepis flavida*).

Growing It: A versatile tree, compact, fairly fast growing and probably the hardiest of all native beeches, capable of withstanding heavy frosts, snow and intense rainfall. Will grow in poor soil. Good for bonsai cultivation and in rock gardens. Seed ripe in early autumn.

SMALL

UNTOOTHED

LEAVES ALTERNATING

43

Kānuka
White Tea Tree

Kunzea ericoides [Family: Myrtaceae]

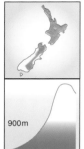

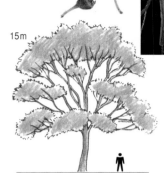

15m

900m

Leaves:	About 1 cm long, *soft to touch, no prickly tip* (unlike mānuka)
Flowers:	Profuse in summer, very fragrant, white, in *clusters* (unlike mānuka), *less than* 6 mm across (unlike mānuka)
Seeds:	Narrower, longer capsules than mānuka
Trunk:	Grows taller than mānuka; thin peeling bark

Apparently named after a hard-wooded Tahitian shrub
anua (silky myrtle). The many medicinal uses of kānuka include the use of pounded seed capsules to make a poultice for running sores. This, in my experience, does work. Indeed, research confirms that it is effective against a common drug-resistant bacterium, golden staph (*Staphylococcus aureus*). The oil is now commercially available. Kānuka also contains *leptospermone*, an insecticide and an effective remedy for intestinal worms. Better known
however is the use of kānuka (and mānuka) leaves for brewing tea – a use that began with Captain Cook. A teaspoonful of fresh, young leaves per cup is plenty. Māori valued the timber for making the shafts of bird spears, weapons and paddles, and used its inner bark as a durable and waterproof roofing material. Kānuka subsequently became a favoured outdoor timber for house and marine piles etc., for the spokes of horse-drawn coaches and wagons, and for tool and implement handles. However, its use as firewood has unfortunately since led to its complete destruction in many areas.

Nature Notes: On summer nights, many species of moth visit the flowers for nectar; by day, green gecko, bellbirds, honey bees and beetles (including 'large pintail beetle' and 'mānuka chafer') assist pollination. Kākāriki (parakeets) consume flowerbuds and flowers; in winter, kererū eat the leaves. Small capsules release fine wind-borne seeds. Saddlebacks tear off outer bark in search of insects and use twigs as nesting material. The branches are a good place to find 'old man's beard' lichen, stick insects and 'kānuka longhorn' beetle. So far, 16 species of moth caterpillars have been recorded from the plant, including four specialists: two 'kānuka loopers', a 'kānuka leaf-tyer' and a 'kānuka leafminer'. The tree also supports a 'tea tree scale' insect, a 'tea tree seed bug', a 'tea tree mirid' insect, three 'kānuka mirid' insects, two 'kānuka psyllid' insects and a 'kānuka gall mite'. Though small, the flowers and leaves are relished by possums. Not eaten by goats. Plays an important role in erosion control and forest regeneration.

Growing It: The great mass of white flowers makes kānuka a good specimen tree, with the advantage of being resistant to the sooty 'mānuka blight fungus'. Quick from seed or semi-hardwood cuttings.

Mānuka Tea Tree

Leptospermum scoparium [Family: Myrtaceae]

8 m

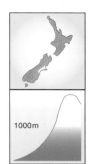

1000m

Leaves:	About 1 cm long, *stiff, tip prickly to touch* (unlike kānuka)
Flowers:	Prolific in late spring, usually white (sometimes pink), *more than* 6 mm across (unlike kānuka)
Seeds:	In hard *broad* seed capsules (unlike kānuka)
Other:	Grows to just 8 m high (unlike kānuka), exuding a wonderful smell at the peak of summer

Also known as **kātoa** or **kahikātoa** (ka-hika-a-toa), 'hika' meaning 'kindle fire by friction'; 'toa' meaning 'warrior'. 'Mānuka' also means 'weapon'. However, straight poles supplied not only weapons and bird-spear shafts, but also battens, rafters, paddles and garden implements. Flexible seedlings were used for making traps for eels and crayfish, and sheets of bark used for roofing and capes or folded to make water containers. Māori also collected a sweet, gum-like deposit from the trunk as food (a bit like damp icing sugar), using the true gummy sap for scenting hair oil. The European name derives from Captain Cook and his crew who brewed the leaves into tea and beer. Settlers cut twigs as brooms, used the bark for dyeing wool, cut stems for hop poles, tool and implement handles or quality firewood, and used the sawdust for smoking fish. Its essential oil is used these days for skin care, in soap-making and as perfume. Mānuka honey tastes excellent and possesses antibacterial properties. The plant also contains an insecticidal compound (*leptospermone*).

Nature Notes: At night, many moths visit the flowers for nectar; by day, common green gecko, honey bees, flies and beetles (including the 'large pintail beetle' and 'mānuka chafer', below left and right) also assist pollination. Broad capsules release fine, wind-borne seeds. Leaves eaten by kererū; leaves and seed capsules important foods of kākāpō. Possums relish flowers and leaves. Saddlebacks and kōkako tear off papery bark as nesting material. Conspicuous insects eating leaves in summer include 'mānuka chafer' beetle, at least six species of stick insect (including the 'common stick insect'),'orange & black longhorn' beetle (right; common on and around flowers) and the 'kānuka longhorn' (on deadwood). Caterpillars of at least eight kinds of native moths have been recorded here and several specialist invertebrates: a 'tea tree mirid insect', five 'tea tree scale' insects, a 'tea tree psyllid', two 'mānuka mealybugs' and a 'mānuka gall mite' (which causes 'witches' broom' deformation of stems). The 'soot' on some trees is a 'mānuka blight fungus' growing on the honeydew of an Australian scale insect. A small-flowered mistletoe is also sometimes seen on the branches.

Growing It: Quick from seed or semi-hardwood cuttings. Good nursery plant for forest regeneration.

Tōtara

Podocarpus totara [Family: Podocarpaceae]

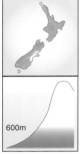
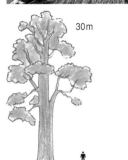

30m

600m

Leaves:	Stiff, *prickly* to touch, *not in 2 rows* (unlike mataī and miro), up to 2.5 cm long (longer on seedling trees)
Fruit:	Green seed on juicy red base (on female trees only) in autumn
Trunk:	Stringy red-brown bark
Other:	The longer-leaved **Hall's tōtara** is more common in the south and at higher altitudes

A 'rākau rangatira' (chiefly tree) of Māori, from which huge war canoes capable of carrying 100 warriors were – and still are – hollowed out from a single log. Tōtara has also been the preferred wood for large carvings, bowls and framing for whare. Microscopic analysis of museum artefacts shows that the branch wood was used for axe handles and beaters. Sheets of inner bark were used as roofing or ingeniously folded as water containers, or used as splints to support fractured bones. 'Tōtara' has a double meaning, the spiky leaves likening it to the porcupine fish (tōtara) of east Polynesia, but with 'tō' meaning 'drag', and 'tara' meaning 'spike', this name also recalls the use of a pointed tōtara stick to produce fire by friction. Māori vigorously scraped this sharpened stick on a slab of softer wood such as māhoe or patete – see kaikōmako (page 22) for details. Basketloads of bright red tōtara fruit were collected by Māori as a favourite food. The flavour of the seeds are too piney, but the red juicy part tastes sweet, with only a slight flavour of pine. The boiled bark and smoke from burning wood were both used medicinally. Huge areas of tōtara were subsequently felled to supply timber for general building purposes, railway sleepers, bridges, wharves, and telephone poles. Nowadays, the odd piece of wood is used for carving and furniture. Homespinners have used the bark to produce a dye.

Nature Notes: September–October, two 'native catkin weevils' feed in the pollen cones, alongside bees. Tūī, kererū, bellbirds, kōkako and weka eat the fruit. Conspicuous insects include 'prickly stick insect', 'pallid longhorn' beetle (on dead and dying twigs) and caterpillars of six native moths (including those of a specialist 'tōtara leafminer moth' tunnelling the leaves). Other specialists include a 'tōtara gall mite', 'tōtara thrips', 'tōtara gall midge', 'tōtara mirid', 'tōtara aphid' and 'tōtara scale'. Avoided by goats but can be heavily browsed by possums, which leave territorial scratch marks on the trunks. A lichen is common on the leaves, the yellow-fruited mistletoe (*Ileostylis micranthus*) in the branches and the cosmopolitan 'yellow paint lichen' (*Chrysothrix candelaris*) on the bark.

Growing It: Grown in the open as a specimen tree, a young tōtara bears branches and leaves right down to the ground. Can also be grown as a hedge plant. Grows easily from fresh seed or tip cuttings. Relatively fast growing, very hardy, tolerant of both wet and dry conditions, and will withstand wind.

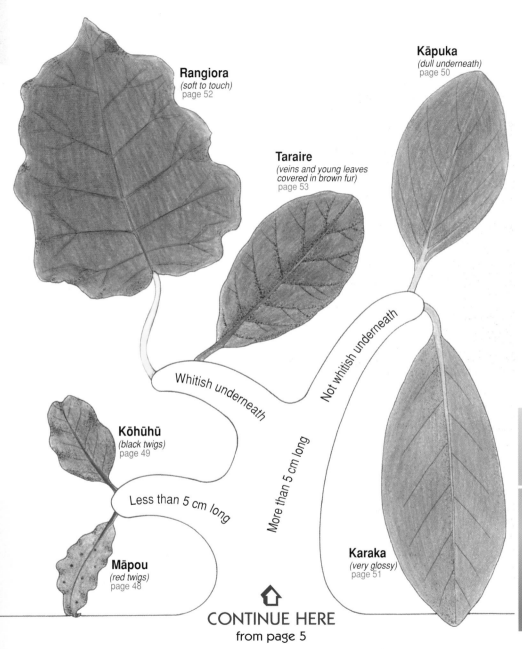

Rangiora
(soft to touch)
page 52

Kāpuka
(dull underneath)
page 50

Taraire
(veins and young leaves covered in brown fur)
page 53

Whitish underneath

Not whitish underneath

Kōhūhū
(black twigs)
page 49

Less than 5 cm long

More than 5 cm long

Māpou
(red twigs)
page 48

Karaka
(very glossy)
page 51

⬆
CONTINUE HERE
from page 5

LEAVES ALTERNATING UNTOOTHED

YOU CAN MEASURE YOUR LEAF HERE
├─── 5 cm ───┤

Māpou
Red Matipo

Myrsine australis [Family: Myrsinaceae]

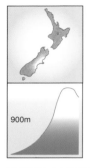

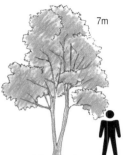

7m

900m

Leaves:	Distinctly *wavy-edged*, reddish on new growth, often with little reddish blotches (unlike kōhūhū), mostly 2–5 cm long
Fruit:	Very small, almost black, borne on stem (on female trees only) in summer
Other:	*Young stems red* (unlike kōhūhū)

The main Māori use of this tree was ceremonial, young plants being pulled from the ground to perform karakia or prayers; this is the origin of the name, 'mā' here meaning 'freed from tapu' and 'pou' being 'a pole used for incantations'. Sectioning and light-microscope analysis of museum artefacts reveals that Māori also used the tree's exceptionally strong wood for composite adze handle sockets. Later, cabinetmakers used the pale, red-veined timber for wooden chairs, handles of chisels and other carpenter's tools, and as a veneer. While not durable in contact with the ground, timber from larger trees was sometimes used for rafters, beams and joists. However, its most popular use has probably been as firewood. The English name, red matipo, is a corruption of an alternative Māori one (**matipou**), 'red' referring to the distinctive colouring of leaves and stems, due to *anthocyanins* that are thought to help protect the plant from the damaging effects of strong sunlight. In Māori medicine (rongoā), māpou leaves were boiled to make an infusion for toothache. Leaves are known to contain *rutin*, which is used in the relief of arthritic problems. Māpou also contains *embelin* which has been used elsewhere as a remedy for skin disease, intestinal worms and as a general tonic.

Nature Notes: The inconspicuous flowers are thought to be wind-pollinated. Fruit eaten by tūī, bellbirds, kererū, kōkako, kākāriki, whiteheads and tauhou (silvereyes). Seeds cracked and eaten by kākā (top centre). Caterpillars of three native generalist moths: 'black-headed leafroller', 'long-snouted leafroller' and 'sharp-tipped bell moth' web leaves together. The tree also supports a 'māpou jewel beetle', a 'māpou bark weevil', two 'māpou scale' insects, a 'māpou mealybug', two 'māpou gall flies' and three kinds of specialist mite (one in pale blisters on the underside of leaves, one that rolls edges of leaves, and a third that distorts leaves). Eaten by deer, and often by possums too.

Growing It: A hardy tree or shrub that can take quite severe pruning, making it a popular hedge or shrub border plant in well-drained soil. Resistant to wind. Also suitable as a specimen or background tree. Easily grown from seed; can also be raised from semi-hardwood cuttings. Quick growing.

Kōhūhū

Pittosporum tenuifolium [Family: Pittosporaceae]

8m

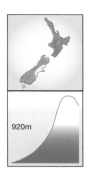

920m

Leaves:	*3–6 cm long* (unlike tarata), sweet smell when crushed, *often with wavy edges*
Flowers:	Small, very dark red to almost black; sweet-smelling at night (late spring)
Fruit:	Round, dark seed capsule, splitting to reveal stiky black seeds (ripe in late autumn)
Other:	*Stems dark or black* (unlike māpou)

Also known as **kohukohu**. An alternative name **tāwhiri** refers to a sprig being waved ceremoniously to signal welcome ('tāwhiri' meaning 'to bid welcome'). Māori made short, vertical cuts in the trunk or bruised the bark to collect a perfumed gum (also known as tāwhiri) used for scenting hair oil from crushed tītoki seeds and in ointments made from kererū fat (New Zealand pigeon). The bled gum was also mixed with the bitter, dried sap of pūhā (sow thistle) for use as a form of chewing gum. The leaves of kōhūhū were similarly used in scent sachets. Medicinally, the plant (presumably a decoction from the leaves) was used for treating scabies, eczema of the scalp and other skin diseases. As a timber, kōhūhū carries the distinction of being almost twice as strong as English oak, but lacks durability in the ground, and this limited its usefulness. The tiny, dark purple, flowers have been used as a source of a grass-green dye. Another name, **black matipo**, likens the foliage to a matipou (page 48) but with black stems.

Nature Notes: At night the flowers are visited by noctuid moths; by day, by tūī, bellbirds, stitchbirds, bristle flies and honey bees. Kākā, pōpokotea (whiteheads) and silvereyes eat the sticky seeds, which often attach themselves to feathers to hitch a ride. Trees can be affected by the same phytoplasma disease affecting cabbage trees. Conspicuous insects found here include at least 13 species of 'longhorn beetle', four of them specialists; a 'Pittosporum shield bug', a 'Pittosporum psyllid' (which forms conspicuous lumps on leaves), caterpillars of a 'Pittosporum leafminer moth' (which tunnel within the leaf) and caterpillars of two leaf-tyer moths, including a 'Pittosporum leaf-tyer'. Also supports two

'kōhūhū gall mites', a 'kōhūhū gall midge', a 'kōhūhū flower weevil', a 'kōhūhū flowerbud weevil', a 'kōhūhū dead branch weevil', a 'Pittosporum bark weevil' and a 'Pittosporum leafminer weevil' (which leaves brown blotches on the leaves). Trees are freely browsed by both goats and possums.

Growing It: Useful shrub, hedge or small tree in well-drained soil. Hardy with attractive foliage and sweet flower scent; attractive to birds. Sprigs cut from hedge plants in Cornwall, England, are even sold in the London flower markets. Several cultivated varieties are available. Best grown from seed.

Kāpuka/ Pāpāuma Broadleaf

Griselinia littoralis [Family: Cornaceae]

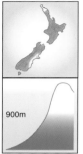
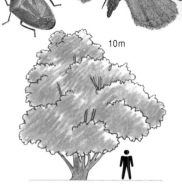

10m

900m

Leaves:	Often *slightly* unequal at base (on the closely related **akapuka**, the base is *very* unequal-sided), dark green on top, *never shiny below* (unlike karaka)
Fruit:	Very small, purple-black (on female trees only) in autumn
Trunk:	Short and gnarled

The tiny berries (huariki) taste decidedly bitter but, when ripe, were reportedly eaten in lean times by Māori. The inner bark was used as a remedy for certain types of tuberculosis and sexually transmitted diseases. More recently, homespinners have produced khaki and grey shades, presumably also from the bark. European settlers selected the red timber for its durability, especially for house piles, fence posts and railway sleepers. The difficulty of finding much length of straight trunk frustrated most timber workers, but boatbuilders quickly turned this feature to their advantage. The name, pāpāuma, links the tree with pauma, the Rarotongan red mistletoe, which bears similar leaves and fruit. Apart from the **akapuka** mentioned below, the plant's true relatives (*Griselinia*) are found only in Chile.

Nature Notes: In spring, clusters of small white flowers flag the attention of small pollinating flies and nectar-feeding birds: tūī, bellbirds and stitchbirds. Honey bees collect pollen. Bellbirds and tūī also eat the fruit, as do kererū (which eat the leaves too). Kākā strip bark to collect sap, while kōkako take leaves to a safe perch to pick off scale insects. Other conspicuous insects on the plant include the native green 'New Zealand vegetable bug' (sucks sap), 'tree wētā' (eat leaves at night); the 'hissing longhorn' beetle; caterpillars of eight native 'leaf-tyer moths' (which web leaves together); and caterpillars of the 'common forest looper' moth (top right). The tree also supports two 'kāpuka gall mites' and a 'Griselinia leafminer weevil'. Frequently browsed by possums, goats, wild cattle and deer; indeed, deer commonly eat large quantities of yellow fallen leaves too, especially in autumn. Norway rats chew the bark.

Growing It: As a garden tree or shrub, kāpuka offers attractive foliage and a tolerance of persistent winds and salt spray. Takes heavy pruning, making it a popular hedge plant too. Grown easily from seed or semi-hardwood cuttings. Though quick growing, can live for over 100 years. The closely-related **akapuka** (*Griselinia lucida*, also known as **puka**) – considered by many to be more attractive – is also widely cultivated but requires better soil. This has larger, much glossier leaves, conspicuously unequal-sided where the base of the leaf meets the leaf stalk.

Karaka

Corynocarpus laevigatus [Family: Corynocarpaceae]

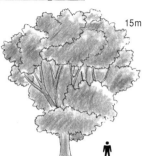

15m

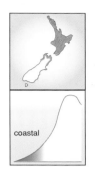

coastal

Leaves: Dark green, *very glossy*, glossy beneath (unlike kāpuka), opposite (unlike kāpuka), *edges tightly curled under*, no teeth, large, 10–15 cm long

Fruit: Orange when ripe, 2.5–4 cm long (summer)

Trunk: Smooth and grey-brown

The name **kōpī** is also used on the Chatham Islands and elsewhere, often for the fruit, in particular. In some interpretations of Māori oral history Māori are said to have brought this tree to Aotearoa from tropical Polynesia; however, the material evidence contradicts this. The *name* of the tree *was,* however, brought from tropical Polynesia and there is firm evidence that Māori transported the seed around New Zealand – one of the few trees to be cultivated by them. The properly prepared kernels of the berries were an important food. Raw kernels not only taste unpalatable but are highly poisonous, causing violent convulsions followed by permanent paralysis. Traditionally, several days' cooking in a hāngi and several weeks' soaking in a running stream were used to render them safe. I would describe their taste as being like sweet chestnut. In thermal areas, an alternative cooking method involved leaving baskets of ripe fruit in a boiling spring for about 18 hours, before carefully rinsing them. The kernels contain *karakin, caronarian* and *cibarian*, all of which are also known to kill grass grub larvae – a property that may have commercial applications. Leaves placed on wounds are said to be healing, provided the upper surface is in contact with the wound; reversed, they draw out pus. Māori used the timber for canoes, but it is otherwise regarded as useless – except as firewood.

Nature Notes: August–December, bellbirds visit the small flowers – along with honey bees and many flies. By eating the fruit whole, kererū (New Zealand pigeons) help disperse the seed, as feeding lizards may also do. Tūī and kākā consume the fruit too, but ship rats and kiore eat only the flesh. Possums feed on the fruit too, but rarely on the leaves. Other conspicuous insects include caterpillars of three native 'leaf-tyer moths' which web leaves together. On dead wood, the 7-cm-long 'giraffe weevil' and several native longhorn beetles – 'grey longhorn', 'striped longhorn', 'lemon tree borer' and 'squeaking longhorn'. The tree also supports a 'karaka gall mite' and 'karaka deadwood weevil'.

Growing It: Useful as shelter or for its attractive foliage and large, orange fruit. Grows easily from fresh seed (germinates quickly). To thrive, it requires a rich, well-drained soil.

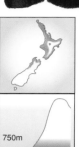
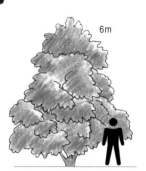

Rangiora

Brachyglottis repanda [Family: Asteraceae]

6m

750m

Leaves:	Very large and soft, mostly 10–20 cm long, *white beneath*, with wavy edges
Flowers:	Creamy white, in large clusters, sweet smelling (spring)
Other:	The long leaf stalks are also white

An emblem of life to Māori. Scholars have translated the name as 'living sky', but the fact that the tree's flowering signalled the fourth month of the Māori calendar (September) – time to plant the kūmara crop – suggests an alternative translation, from 'ora' (safe) and 'rangi' (weather, or period of time). The generous size of the leaves and their flexibility made them useful for wrapping hāngi meals and as lids to cover preserved food. Early observers suggested that a particularly broad-leaved form was also traditionally cultivated. Such uses may render the European names, **bushman's friend** (or **bushman's toilet paper**), inappropriate. The leaves are perhaps better promoted as notepaper. Indeed one Christmas, I received one with a drawing on the bright underside as a card; others have been addressed, stamped and sent through the post. Māori used pieces of leaf to feather toetoe spears, and applied them to wounds and old ulcerated sores. The gum, though apparently poisonous, was chewed (but never swallowed) as a kind of chewing gum and as a cure for bad breath. Māori made cuts in the bark to collect this gum, and then heated it in tītoki seed oil or pigeon fat until dissolved to make a scented hair oil or for ointments.

Nature Notes: Clusters of spring flowers flag the attention of small pollinating beetles, including native 'leaf beetles'. Honey bees collect nectar and occasionally, in February, a kind of honeydew on the trunks. Other conspicuous insects include the 'giraffe weevil' and 'lemon tree borer' beetle, the 'rangiora psyllid' (which distorts young leaves); several native moth caterpillars, including those of the 'silver Y moth', 'sharp-tipped bell moth' and the 'woolly bear' caterpillars of the 'magpie moth' (top), but also several specialists: caterpillars of the 'rangiora leafminer moth' (tunnelling within the leaf), 'rangiora metalmark moth' (rolls edges of leaves), and two similar 'rangiora looper' moths (one on the South Island and this one on the North – right). Rangiora is freely browsed by goats and cattle, but rarely by possums.

Growing It: Its striking leaves make this a good specimen tree. Can also be planted as part of a shrub border and pruned if necessary. Requires good drainage and somewhat frost tender (especially when young) but will tolerate wind. Grows easily from cuttings.

Taraire

Beilschmiedia tarairi [Family: Lauraceae]

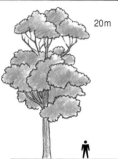

20m

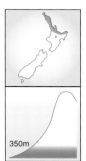

350m

Leaves:	Dark green above, leathery, usually whitish beneath, mostly 7–14 cm long
Fruit:	3.5 cm long, dark purple (autumn)
Other:	Buds, new branches and leaf veins all covered in *fine brown fuzz*

Named after the tropical almond (taraire) of east Polynesia, which bears similar leaves and edible nuts. The large kernel of the New Zealand tree was a staple food of northern forest-dwelling Māori. The largish, purple-black fruit has a thin flesh that tastes strongly of turpentine, sweet enough that it was occasionally eaten – generally only by children, though. Traditionally, the kernels were steamed for a couple of days in a hāngi, but they can also be boiled for an hour or roasted in the embers of a campfire. The texture of these I would describe as a slimy version of a potato – although roasting greatly reduces the sliminess. In the right season (autumn) they can provide a worthwhile meal. Untreated heartwood will last for interior use but untreated sapwood is subject to borer attack. An easy timber to saw, machine and turn, taking a good finish, taraire is well-suited to its 19th century uses of furniture-making, picture frames, the manufacture of ships' blocks and light carts. The wood has also occasionally been used for interior finishing of houses and, with preservative treatment, for sub-floor framing. It is straight-grained but unfortunately brittle and prone to split. Though it was sometimes offered for sale as firewood, it tends to burn too quickly.

Nature Notes: Stitchbirds and honey bees visit the inconspicuous flowers in spring. Kererū (New Zealand pigeon) eat the fruit, helping to spread the seed (as lizards may also do) – that is, if possums have not got to them first. Other conspicuous insects found on the tree include a native 'leaf beetle' chewing young leaves; 7-cm-long 'giraffe weevils' on dead wood; and the 'elephant weevil' which, on summer nights, is seen crawling on the trunk, feeding on the sap. The tree also supports several specialist invertebrates including the 'taraire gall mite', 'taraire mirid', 'taraire weevil' and 'taraire scale'.

Growing It: A shapely specimen tree with fine, bold foliage, grown successfully as far south as Christchurch when protected from frost. Generally grown from seed. Does best in a rich, well-drained soil, in a slightly sheltered and shady position. Quick to germinate, relatively quick growing and an ideal tree for attracting kererū (New Zealand pigeons).

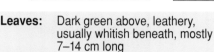

LEAVES ALTERNATING UNTOOTHED BROAD

Kauri

Agathis australis [Family: Araucariaceae]

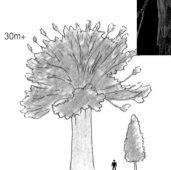

30m+

600m

Leaves:	Alternating to almost opposite, mostly 2–4 cm long (though longer on young trees)
Cones:	Round female cones containing winged seeds (above); male cones finger-shaped (spring to summer)
Trunk:	Hammer-marked, mostly grey, falling in large, thick flakes
Other:	Bleeding gum common on or under the tree

A chiefly tree of Māori, whose trunk was likened to the body of a sperm whale. The Polynesian origin of the Māori name, kauri, remains unknown but its use has spread from New Zealand now to related trees (*Agathis*) in Fiji, Queensland, New Caledonia and Papua New Guinea. Northern Māori prized the wood for large carvings and canoes, using branch wood for mallets, weapons and spades. Fresh kauri gum (kāpia) was valued for chewing, scrapings of harder gum (below) used as a fire kindler or torch fuel and burnt to produce a tattooing pigment and to kill or deter pest insects in kūmara plantations. Europeans felled most of the accessible old trees, valuing the timber for its branch-free trunk, using it widely for house-, ship- and cart-building, also for church pews and post office counters. Stumps and demolition kauri remain popular with the woodturner. The gum was exported commercially; its use involved dissolving the fresh, milky gum or clear, sub-fossilised resin in linseed oil to make varnish and as a raw material in paint and linoleum. Harder, more transparent pieces were shaped into mouthpieces for smokers' pipes. Kauri gum was even an ingredient of a compound used for taking impressions for making dentures. Fossil evidence indicates that the tree once grew as far south as Invercargill.

Nature Notes: Forks provide sites for roosting short-tailed bats and perching plants. A 1938 study found 53 kinds of ferns and seed plants up here (38 of them in a single tree). Kākā, kākāriki and eastern rosellas tear open cones to crack and eat the winged seeds (above). In late autumn and early winter, fallen seeds eaten by mice may affect kauri regeneration. Tiny caterpillars of 'kauri leafminer moth' tunnel inside green leaves, leaving meandering silver lines, and on the leaves, looper caterpillars of a native conifer looper moth. On the wood can be found 'elephant weevil', 'giraffe weevil', native longhorn beetles and three specialist 'kauri weevils'. When kakapō were on Little Barrier Island, chicks and adults ate the leaves. In 2008, 'kauri diebark' (a *Phytophthora* disease) was recognised.

Growing It: An attractive specimen tree while still young and neatly conical – a form that it retains for at least 50 years. Requires good drainage and is fast-growing in good soil. Easy to grow from fresh seed – pick the round, female cones when mature (in March) and leave in the sun until they ripen and fall apart to release the small, winged seeds. Sow within three weeks. Quick to germinate.

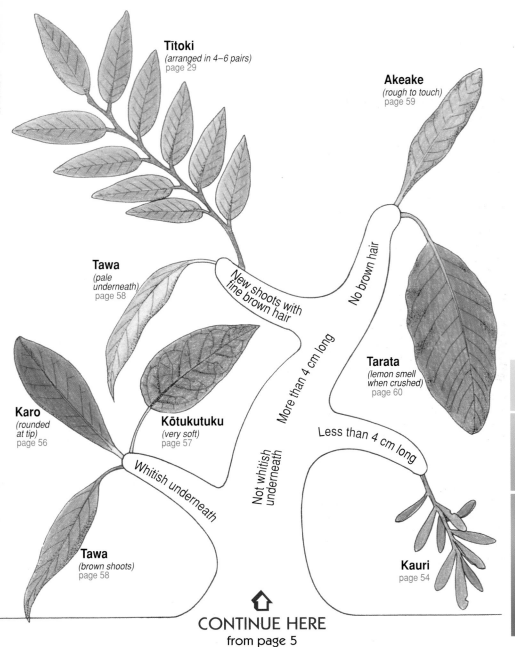

Tītoki
(arranged in 4–6 pairs)
page 29

Akeake
(rough to touch)
page 59

Tawa
(pale underneath)
page 58

New shoots with fine brown hair

No brown hair

More than 4 cm long

Tarata
(lemon smell when crushed)
page 60

Karo
(rounded at tip)
page 56

Kōtukutuku
(very soft)
page 57

Whitish underneath

Not whitish underneath

Less than 4 cm long

Tawa
(brown shoots)
page 58

Kauri
page 54

⬆
CONTINUE HERE
from page 5

YOU CAN MEASURE YOUR LEAF HERE
⊢——— 4 cm ———⊣

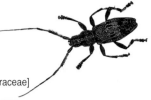

Karo
Pittosporum crassifolium [Family: Pittosporaceae]

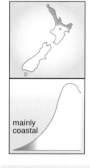

mainly coastal

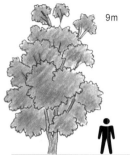

9m

Leaves:	*Alternating* (unlike pōhutukawa, page 15), *whitish beneath*, 4–7 cm long
Flowers:	Red to purple, about 1 cm across (mainly early spring); heavily scented – in the evening especially
Fruit:	Round and green, about 2 cm across, bursting to reveal sticky black seeds (autumn)

The names, karo and **kaikaro** mean 'a protective spell' suggesting that the tree's tapu nature was shared with its close relative, kōhūhū. Karo is also the name of a traditional black dye from the tree (obtained most likely from the seeds). The use of the white timber, though very tough, has been confined mostly in marquetry or inlaying; it does not rank as a good firewood. The tree's flowering did, however, serve as one of the spring seasonal markers of coastal Māori, helping to define the fourth month of their calendar (September).

Nature Notes: A rich scent produced by the flowers on still evenings in early spring attracts honey bees and several species of fly and – by night – noctuid moths. By day, tūī, bellbirds, stitchbirds, kererū and kākā come for the nectar. The three- or four-part capsules split to reveal sticky seeds attractive to tūī, kererū, kākā, kākāriki and rats – the glue ensures that these creatures provide the seeds with an effective means of dispersal. In the case of rats, though, the seeds are clearly being destroyed. Bumps clearly visible on some leaves (see below) are made by the nymphs (young stage) of an insect known as the 'Pittosporum psyllid'. Other conspicuous insects found here include the 'Pittosporum shield bug' (top left), a web-tyer caterpillar and several longhorn beetles: the 'squeaking longhorn', 'lemon tree borer', 'grey longhorn', 'pittosporum longhorn' and two other native longhorns. The tree also supports a 'Pittosporum bark beetle', a 'Pittosporum weevil' and a 'karo weevil'. At night, a sticky honeydew on the plants is harvested by the Pacific gecko.

Growing It: Versatile and attractive as an ornamental and shelter tree, its extreme resistance to strong salt winds making it especially suited to coastal situations. Easy to grow and fast, making it useful for revegetation projects in well-drained soil. From as far back as the late 19th century it has been recommended for helping to stabilise inland sand dunes. Its ability to withstand trimming also makes it popular for hedges both locally and as far afield as Cornwall, England. Germinates easily from fallen seed and transplants well. Growing from cuttings is more difficult.

Kōtukutuku
Tree Fuchsia

Fuchsia excorticata [Family: Onagraceae]

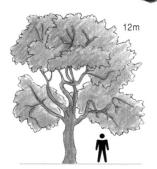

12m

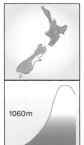

1060m

Leaves:	Few or no teeth, *white beneath with furry veins, soft. Loses its leaves in southern winters*
Flowers:	Dark purple, hanging – sometimes directly from the trunk (late spring)
Fruit:	Dark purple to almost black, narrow and about 1 cm long (summer)
Trunk:	*Loose papery bark*

The world's tallest fuchsia. Kōtukutuku has been translated as referring to the tree letting go (tukutuku) of its leaves in winter; however, the white underside of these leaves also links the tree to the kōtuku (Pacific flag tree) of Rarotonga, a tree which is in turn named after the white tropical phase of the reef heron (kōtuku). The sweet, edible fruit is known as **kōnini** – a term used by Taranaki Māori to refer to the tree itself. This fruit was eaten raw by Māori. Europeans enjoyed it as jam or stewed with honey or in the form of a pudding. The berries also make a good ink. Homespinners used the bark or decayed wood to produce a range of dyes. The timber is strong and durable, and was prized for ornamental uses including woodturning, but its gnarled nature saved it from large-scale exploitation. Like putaputāwētā and rewarewa, it was nicknamed **bucket-of-water tree**, as even dry wood is almost impossible to burn. To Māori, its flowering signalled the fourth month of their calendar (September), time for planting kūmara. The tree was used medicinally as an ingredient in vapour baths by women after childbirth.

Nature Notes: Honey bees collect the nectar, but the tree is primarily pollinated by birds: tūī, bellbirds, stitchbirds, kererū, tauhou (silvereyes) and blackbirds, many of these birds seen wearing the plant's distinctive blue pollen on their foreheads (left). Kererū, tūī, kākāriki, stitchbirds, kōkako, whiteheads, weka, thrushes and possums feed on the fruit, as did the now-extinct piopio (New Zealand thrush). Possums (attracted to *phenols* in the plant) will strip entire trees of leaves, devouring seedlings too; by 1970, 85% of these trees in the Urewera Forest had been killed by them. Freely eaten by deer and cattle too, and goats, which will even climb out along sloping trunks to browse. Conspicuous insects here (in spring and summer) include the 'forest shield bug' (top left), caterpillars of the 'green carpet owlet' and caterpillars of four kinds of leaf-tyer moths. The tree also supports three 'kōtukutuku weevils', a 'native fuchsia psyllid' (on young shoots) and two 'kōtukutuku gall mites' (on distorted young leaves).

Growing It: Grown for its gnarled trunk and papery bark. Easily grown from seed or cuttings. Fast-growing but will not tolerate drought or strong wind. In the south, it loses its leaves in winter.

57

Tawa

Beilschmiedia tawa [Family: Lauraceae]

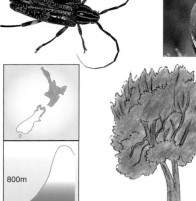

24m+

800m

Leaves:	6–10 cm long, alternating to almost opposite, *pale to white beneath*; hanging, graceful and willow-like, *brown fur* on new growth
Fruit:	Dark purple to black, 2–3 cm long (late summer)
Trunk:	Dark, smooth. Older trees often buttressed at base

Named after tava, the Pacific lychee of tropical Polynesia, the flesh of whose fruit was also eaten. When perfectly ripe, the purple-black flesh of the New Zealand tawa has a sweetish, slightly turpentine flavour. But it was the cooked kernels that were most prized as food – sometimes dried and stored for years as a standby. These were usually steamed in a hāngi for two days, or occasionally boiled or roasted in embers, and (like taraire berries) taste similar to potato but with a slimy texture. Roasted, they taste better. Ripe fruit will also dye wool purple or green depending on the mordant used. The bark was used medicinally for stomach pain and colds; 19th century trampers infused the bark to make a sweet tea. Māori used the wood for paddles, long shafts of bird spears, and battens for the roofs and walls of whare (buildings). Large-scale use of the timber began in the 1800s with coopers making dairy buckets and tubs, casks and butter kegs. It has also been widely used for woodturning, clothes pegs, furniture and flooring, papermaking and firewood. Indeed, up until 1991, rather than using plantation trees for the purpose, natural tawa forests were still being felled for wood pulp.

Nature Notes: In spring, tiny green flowers attract stitchbirds and bees. The fruit is popular with kākā, kōkako, kākāpō, wild pigs, rats and possums; however, only kererū (New Zealand pigeons) and possibly lizards are capable of spreading whole seeds. Twigs are collected by kōkako as nesting material. On broken branches, large 'variegated longhorn' beetles are found (also on kōwhai). Other conspicuous insects here include the 'spiny longhorn' beetle (45 mm long), 'giraffe weevil' (7 cm long), and three caterpillars of native moths (two loopers, and one that feeds on the large seeds). Leaves favoured by possums, which can defoliate whole trees. Freely browsed by wild cattle. A kind of lichen often grows on the upper surface of the leaf, while the smooth, hard bark supports mosses, lichens and climbing ferns.

Growing It: The delicate, drooping leaves give this tree a graceful appearance, making it a fine specimen tree. Fruiting trees attract birds. Grows easily from seed. Quick to germinate. Prefers a damp, cool site in rich, well-drained soil with moderate shelter from wind.

Akeake

Dodonaea viscosa [Family: Sapindaceae]

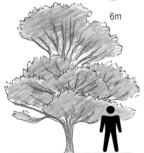

6m

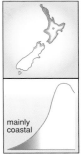

mainly coastal

Leaves:	*Sandpapery to touch* and standing erect (unlike tawa), 4–7 cm long, sometimes reddish
Seeds:	Seed capsules 1.5 cm across with 2–3 wings (on female trees only) in summer
Trunk:	Flaking reddish bark
Other:	Young shoots can be slightly sticky

The ancestors of New Zealand Māori recognised this tree as one that grows naturally also in the tropical Pacific. We know this from the fact that they gave it the name akeake – the same name traditionally used for it on several Polynesian islands, including Niue and the southern Cook Islands. Here, the name was also applied to poor soil for this is indeed where it thrives. European settlers, unfamiliar with it, named it **hop bush** after the likeness of its seeds to a plant of their own homeland. Akeake is one of the hardest native woods, so hard that a falling axe will often literally bounce off it. This remarkable density made it particularly useful to Māori for making fern-root beaters, clubs and other weapons. Likewise, European settlers used it for making heads for mauls used in bush-felling. Indeed, when brass was in short supply, the wood even proved an effective substitute for making machine bearings. Cabinetmakers valued it for inlaid work and picture frames, while sculptors accord it equal status to the more traditional box wood for making modelling tools. Twigs have even been used to produce various dyes (green to bright gold), while the unusual seed capsules are used in flower arranging. Māori are reputed to have used the leaves (or perhaps the lemon-eucalyptus smelling seeds) to make a kind of perfume, but do not seem to have used it medicinally. This is surprising, since the tree is indeed used medicinally in Indonesia, Reunion Island, Kanaky (New Caledonia), Tahiti, Hawai`i, Australia, Panama and Peru – most commonly for reducing fevers.

Nature Notes: September to January, introduced honey bees, bristle flies and several small species of fly visit the inconspicuous flowers. The winged seed capsules are wind-borne. A native 'longhorn beetle' (*Xylotoles laetus*) is sometimes seen for its grubs tunnel into the trunks and thicker branches (of this and other native trees). Specialist insects supported by the tree include the 'akeake psyllid' which feeds on shoot tips, and the 'akeake blister gall midge'. A native mealybug and a couple of native scale insects are also found here.

Growing It: A useful hedge or shelter tree in exposed or coastal areas. Fast-growing; requires a well-drained soil. Grown easily from seed (collected before the capsules open) or from cuttings.

Tarata
Lemonwood
Pittosporum eugenioides [Family: Pittosporaceae]

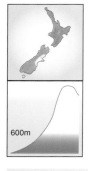

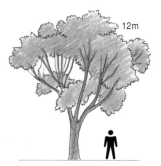

600m

12m

Leaves:	*Lemon-scented when crushed* (unlike tawa), very glossy on top, edges wavy, mid-vein and leaf stalk pale cream, *7–15 cm long* (unlike kōhūhū)
Flowers:	Starry, cream, in bunches, sweet smelling (late spring)
Other:	Grows along streamsides and in open forest

Like its *Pittosporum* cousins, the tree had a tapu use. Tohunga would bless (tara) their pupils by sprinkling (tā) them with a sprig dipped in water. Tara-tā can also be translated as 'spike-cut', for the resinous gum was bled from vertical grooves cut in the trunk and added to heated bird fat or to oil from crushed seeds of tītoki or kōhia (New Zealand passionfruit) to make a scented body lotion. Tarata gum was also chewed with the bitter, dried sap of pūhā (sow thistle) as a chewing gum. Some Māori apparently mixed flowers or crushed leaves with bird fat in the same way. Leaves chewed into a paste were said to make an effective lotion for saddle sores on horses. The timber is strong, tough and elastic, and was chosen by European settlers for the handles of carpenters' tools and woodturning generally. Tarata makes poor firewood.

Nature Notes: At night, the flowers are visited by noctuid moths; by day, by bellbirds, tūī, stitchbirds, flies and honey bees. Kererū and silvereyes eat the seeds, which often get stuck in their beak and feathers. (*Pittosporum* means 'sticky seed'.) The 'Pittosporum psyllid' causes 'pimples' and yellowing on leaves; mines on the underside of leaves are by caterpillars of the 'Pittosporum leafminer moth', and brown blotches by the 'Pittosporum leafmining weevil'. Other conspicuous insects here include the 'Pittosporum shield bug' and 'lemon tree borer' beetle. Tarata also supports a 'tarata leaf gall mite', a 'tarata scale' (leaving pit-marks on the leaf), a 'Pittosporum bark weevil', a 'Pittosporum fruit weevil, a 'Pittosporum longhorn' beetle and caterpillars of the 'tarata looper' moth (top centre) that (make lengthwise marks on the leaf), the 'Pittosporum plume moth' (marks across the leaf) and white 'tarata flat moth' (top right); also found on broadleaf. Possums apparently find the plant unpalatable for they rarely eat it. North of Auckland, a parasitic native mistletoe (tāpia) is sometimes found on the branches.

Growing It: A shapely specimen tree, appreciated for its glossy, wavy-edged leaves and showy, scented flowers. Makes a good hedge or lower tier in a farm shelter belt. Very versatile. Requires well-drained soil. Grown easily and quickly from fully ripened seed.

Conspicuous Flowers and Berries

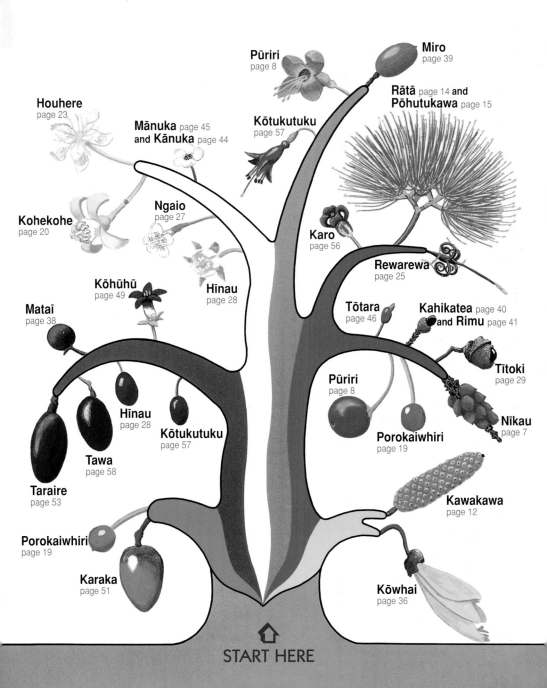

Pūriri
page 8

Miro
page 39

Houhere
page 23

Mānuka page 45
and Kānuka page 44

Kōtukutuku
page 57

Rātā page 14 and
Pōhutukawa page 15

Ngaio
page 27

Karo
page 56

Kohekohe
page 20

Rewarewa
page 25

Kōhūhū
page 49

Hīnau
page 28

Matāi
page 38

Tōtara
page 46

Kahikatea page 40
and Rimu page 41

Hīnau
page 28

Kōtukutuku
page 57

Pūriri
page 8

Tītoki
page 29

Tawa
page 58

Porokaiwhiri
page 19

Nīkau
page 7

Taraire
page 53

Kawakawa
page 12

Porokaiwhiri
page 19

Karaka
page 51

Kōwhai
page 36

⌂
START HERE

Troubleshooting

Are you faced with a very tall, branchless trunk – one whose trunk would take two or more adults to hug? If so, the leaves may be too far out of reach to use the leaf key, so compare the bark with these pictures:

If the bark falls in circular flakes like this, then it is most likely a **kauri** (p. 54), **mataī** (p. 38) or **miro** (p. 39).

If it peels off in long papery strips, like this, then it is most likely a **tōtara** (p. 46).

If it has other kinds of flakes, like this, then it is most likely a **rimu** (p. 41), **kahikatea** (p. 40) or **rātā** (p. 14).

Tip: look on the ground for fallen leaves and use these to follow the leaf key (p. 5).

If you are having trouble matching your leaf with the key:

1. Make sure your leaf is from a **tree**. If it is from a shrub (generally smaller than trees, with no central trunk) you may need to refer to *Which Native Forest Plant?*
2. Are you sure the tree you have found is **native**? If you are in native forest, it most probably will be. But if you found your specimen elsewhere, it may not be.
3. Check that you are looking at a **typical adult** leaf. Leaves do vary, especially between seedling and adult trees.
4. Are you sure the tree is common? Others are not covered.
5. Is it a **tree fern**? Tree ferns are covered in *Which Native Fern?* If you don't have this handy, then check the fronds. Of the tree ferns found on the main islands, the commonest one is ponga (which has silver undersides to its fronds) and mamaku (which has very thick, black frond stems).

If the leaf key is still not working, then take a closer look at the leaf:

1. Are you sure whether or not the leaf has teeth along its edges? The teeth on ngaio and hīnau leaves, for example, are easy to miss.
2. Are you sure whether the leaves are opposite or alternate? At first glance, taraire and kauri leaves may *appear* to be all opposite.
3. Did you remember to start at the bottom of the first leaf key (p. 5)? That's important.

Selected References

Aston, B. C. 'The Indigenous Tans and Vegetable Dyestuffs of New Zealand. Parts I and II.' *N. Z. J. Agriculture* 15: 55–62, 1917; 15: 117–28, 1917 and 16: 358–65, 1918.

Beever, James. *A Dictionary of Maori Plant Names.* Auckland Botanical Society, 1987.

Best, Elsdon. *Forest Lore of the Maori.* Government Printer, 1977.

Best, Elsdon. *The Maori Division of Time.* Government Printer, 1986.

Brockie, Robert. *A Living New Zealand Forest.* Bateman, 1992.

Brooker, S. G., Cambie, R. C. and Cooper, R. C. *Economic Native Plants of New Zealand.* Botany Division, DSIR, 1988.

Brooker, S. G., Cambie, R. C. and Cooper, R. C. *New Zealand Medicinal Plants.* Heinemann, 1987.

Connor, H. E. *The Poisonous Plants in New Zealand.* Government Printer, 1977.

Crowe, Andrew. *A Field Guide to the Native Edible Plants of New Zealand.* Penguin, 2004.

Dawson, John. *Forest Vines to Snow Tussocks: The Story of New Zealand Plants.* Victoria University Press, 1993.

Fisher, Muriel and Power, Elaine. *A Touch of Nature.* Collins, 1980.

Hood, I. A. *An Illustrated Guide to Fungi on Wood in New Zealand.* Auckland University Press, 1992.

Horne, Don. *Mushrooms and Other Fungi of New Zealand.* Reed, 2000.

Hutchinson, Amy. *Plant Dyeing.* The Daily Telegraph Co., Napier, 1941.

King, Carolyn M. (Ed.) *The Handbook of New Zealand Mammals.* Oxford University Press, 2005.

Kirk, T. *The Forest Flora of New Zealand.* Government Printer, 1889.

Laing, R. M. and Blackwell, E. W. *Plants of New Zealand.* Whitcombe and Tombs, 1964.

Lloyd, Joyce. *Dyes from Plants of Australia and New Zealand.* Reed, 1981.

Massey, Brian. *Woodturning in New Zealand.* Government Printer, 1987.

McDermott, Mike. *Woodturning with New Zealand Timbers.* Reed Methuen, 1985.

Metcalf, L. J. *The Cultivation of New Zealand Trees and Shrubs.* Reed Methuen, 1987.

Metcalf, Lawrie. *Know Your New Zealand Trees.* New Holland, 2006.

Milner, Ann. *Natural Wool Dyes and Recipes.* John McIndoe, 1979.

Moore, L. B. and Irwin, J. B. *The Oxford Book of New Zealand Plants.* Oxford University Press, 1978.

Mortimer, John and Bunny. *Trees for the New Zealand Countryside.* Butterworths, 1987.

Orbell, Margaret. *The Natural World of the Māori.* David Bateman, 1996.

Pendergrast, Mick. *Feathers and Fibre.* Penguin, 1984.

Reid, J. S. *New Zealand Building Timbers.* New Zealand Forest Service, 1956.

Richards, E. C. *Our New Zealand Trees and Flowers.* Simpson and Williams, 1956.

Riley, Murdoch. *Māori Healing and Herbal.* Viking Sevenseas, 1994.

Taylor, Rev. Richard. 'Vegetable Productions of New Zealand.' *New Zealand Journal*, pp.68–69, 25 March 1848.

Taylor, Rev. Richard. *A Leaf from the Natural History of New Zealand.* Chapman, 1870.

Te Ara: The Encyclopedia of New Zealand. **http://www.teara.govt.nz/TheBush**

Walsh, R. S. *Nectar and Pollen Sources of New Zealand.* National Beekeepers' Association of New Zealand, 1978.

Williams, David. *Mātauranga Māori and Taonga.* Waitangi Tribunal Publication, 2001.

Williams, Herbert W. *A Dictionary of the Māori Language.* Government Printer, Wellington, 1985.

Ecological information for this book came for the most part from articles in the following specialist journals: *Notornis, New Zealand Journal of Zoology, New Zealand Journal of Botany, New Zealand Journal of Ecology, Transactions and Proceedings of the Royal Society of New Zealand, Forest and Bird, DoC Threatened Species Recovery Plans, Journal of Biogeography, Journal of Applied Ecology, Plant Systematics and Evolution, The Weta* and from the Crop & Food Research invertebrate herbivore–host plant association database: **http://plant-synz.landcareresearch.co.nz** Additional plant–animal interactions were found in photographic form through the Nga Manu Sanctuary website **http://ngamanuimages.org.nz**

For the origins of Māori names, I owe much to the work of Bruce Biggs, including 'A Linguist revisits the New Zealand bush' (In Pawley, A, (Ed.) *Man and a Half: Essays in Pacific Anthropology and Ethnobiology in Honour of Ralph Bulmer,* Memoir No. 48: 67-72, The Polynesian Society, Auckland, 1991; and his unpublished work, *The Comparative Polynesian Lexicon Project* (POLLEX). My own small contribution is from a larger referenced project, yet to be published, involving research into Polynesian languages, provisionally entitled *Māori Nation: A Quest for the Pacific Origins of New Zealand Māori Nature Names.*

Index

A
Akapuka, *see* **Kāpuka**, 50
Akeake, 59

B
Beech, 32, 33, 34, 42, 43
Black Beech, 42
Black Matipo, 49
Black Pine, 38
Broadleaf, 50
Brown Pine, 39
Bucket-of-Water Tree,
    25, 35, 57
Bushman's Friend, 52

C
Cabbage Tree, 6
Celery Pine, 30
Cowleaf, 26

F
Five Finger, 11
Fuchsia, Tree, 57

H
Hall's Tōtara,
    see **Tōtara**, 46
Hard Beech, 32
Hinahina, 26
Hīnau, 28
Hop Bush, 59
Horoeka, 24
Houhere, 23

K
Kahikatea, 40
Kahikātoa, 45
Kaikaro, 56
Kaikōmako, 22
Kaiwētā, 26
Kaiwhiri, 19
Kāmahi, 16
Kānuka, 44
Kāpuka, 50
Karaka, 51
Karo, 56
Kātoa, 45
Kauere, 8
Kauri, 54

Kawakawa, 12
Kohekohe, 20
Kōhūhū, 49
Kohukohu, 49
Kokoeka, 24
Kōnini, 57
Kōpī, 51
Kōtukutuku, 57
Kōwhai, 36

L
Lacebark, 23
Lancewood, 24
Lemonwood, 60

M
Māhoe, 26
Makomako, 18
Mānuka, 45
Māpou, 48
Marbleleaf, 35
Matipou, 48
Mataī, 38
Miro, 39
Mountain Beech, 43
Mountain Five Finger,
    see **Whauwhaupaku**, 11
Mountain Toatoa,
    see **Tānekaha**, 30

N
New Zealand Ash, 29
New Zealand Christmas Tree,
    15
New Zealand
    Honeysuckle, 25
New Zealand Oak, 8
Ngaio, 27
Nīkau, 7

O
Orihou,
    see **Whauwhaupaku**, 11

P
Pāpāuma, 50
Patete or Patē, 10
Pepper Tree, 12
Pigeonwood, 19

Pittosporum, 49, 56, 60
Pōhutukawa, 15
Porokaiwhiri, 19
Puahou, 11
Puka, *see* **Kāpuka**, 50
Pukatea, 17
Pūriri, 8
Putaputāwētā, 35

R
Rangiora, 52
Rātā, 14
Red Beech, 33
Red Matipo, 48
Red Pine, 41
Rewarewa, 25
Rimu, 41

S
Seven Finger, 10
Silver Beech, 34
'Snotty Gob', 11

T
Tānekaha, 30
Taraire, 53
Tarata, 60
Tawa, 58
Tawhai or Tawai, 34
Tawhai Raunui, 32, 33
Tawhai Rauriki, 42, 43
Tāwhiri, 49
Tea Tree, 45
Tī Kōuka, 6
Tītoki, 29
Toatoa, *see* **Tānekaha**, 30
Tokitoki, 29
Toromiro, 39
Tōtara, 46
Tōwai, *see* **Kāmahi**, 16
Tree Fuchsia, 57

W
Whauwhaupaku, 11
Whīnau, 28
White Pine, 40
White Tea Tree, 44
Whiteywood, 26
Wineberry, 18